The 50-Word Stories of 2021 Microfiction for Lovers of Quick Reads 50 Give or Take #1 by Vine Leaves Press

The 50-Word Stories of 2021
Copyright © 2021 Vine Leaves Press

All rights reserved.
Print Edition
ISBN: 978-1-925965-74-2
Published by Vine Leaves Press 2021

Cover design by Jessica Bell
Interior design by Amie McCracken

A catalogue record for this book is available from the National Library of Australia

Praise

"Apparently the best things really do come in small packages."
Peter Snell

"Dollops of humanity...in 50 words."
Elaina Battista-Parsons

"Tiny stories make me laugh, cry, or ponder."
Theresa Milstein

"Like a firecracker—tiny but explosive."
Steve Zettler

"50 sizzling words that open glorious, new worlds."
Cordelia Biddle

"50 is the new 70."
John McCaffrey

"Size does matter. 50 words packs a knock-out punch."
Jean Gill

"When small things matter you take your time."
Adam Byatt

Released

The bullet misses her face; it deflects off the bullhorn she holds to her lips. Despite the hole in her lungs, she continues to chant as many hands lift her up and over the crowd. Then she is free, released now, at last, to be the eye, not the storm.

Carolyn R. Russell lives and writes in West Newbury, MA. *carolynrrussell.com*

The Rockery

Helping his dad build a rockery, Timmie lost his whistle and cried himself to sleep for weeks. Young Timmie was helping his granddad repair the rockery when he spied metal between two rocks. He pulled it out, rinsed it off and blew it. Granddad Tim had tears in his eyes.

Peter Snell was a bookseller and he wears a lot of red in December. Facebook *@Bartons.Bookshop*

Mother/Monarch

Before mom died, she said she'd try to come back as a Monarch butterfly. She admired their bright orange wings and the valor of their annual migration from northern California to Mexico and back. She lived like them, with tenacity and joy. Now she regularly flutters by for a visit.

Sue Jenkins is an artist, designer, and Associate Professor of Design in Pennsylvania, USA. *suejenkinsphotography.com*

Together

You were there, although the disease held you at bay, in abeyance, latent. A spark of life behind the veil of your gaze. I glimpsed it, occasionally. Like when you carried me way out into the surf. Or when I'd stand on your feet and we'd walk and laugh. Together.

Eileen Herbert-Goodall wishes her husband would cave into her request to have more pets. *eileenherbertgoodall.com*

Routine

Despair of evening gives way to terrors of the night, to sleep, disrupted, dreaming of elegance, of past and future nightmares. To wake to morning and rise, to work, to read, to listen for wisdom, to love again and hope for another evening, another night, another dream of another day.

Janet Clare lives in Los Angeles. Her debut novel, *Time is the Longest Distance,* was published by Vine Leaves Press. *janetclare.com*

1982

I remember me and BamBam on Ventura Boulevard, laid down in the middle of the street, while the world was fast asleep. I stared at the stars. I whipped my head back and forth in case of cars. It was 4 am. She was my new best friend.

E.H. Kupinsky's resume would only tell you what jobs she took to pay bills while being a better Mom than the one she had. Instagram *@emmysez*

Roughing It

He beckoned to follow as he shot up a steep circular stairwell of half-steps fashioned by Dr. Seuss. I tripped on the third-floor landing despite clinging to the railing *How much further to my room?* I asked. The local mountain climber replied, *Plan the next step. Only that.*

Houston-based poet Margo Davis says her massive air plant is thriving on The Triplets of Belleville soundtrack.

Raindrops

I wake to pattering raindrops and smile, stretching. The light coming through the window is glossy, filtered, hazy. I make coffee and call in sick—a mental health day. I tie my hair back and pick a book off the shelf.

Amie McCracken edits and typesets novels for self-published authors and helps writers polish their work. *amiemccracken.com*

Flesh

I drop my wedding ring in holy water. I hope it repels the years of hate and hope, so I can finally relate to the son we made.

Jessica Bell is the publisher of Vine Leaves Press. Check out all her other personalities at *iamjessicabell.com*.

Preparation

Mother folds towels from the dryer. I'm given hankies. My hands filled with holiday excitement, I drop most. "Don't get too excited," she warns, "you'll only be disappointed." The dryer's drone surrounds us. Christmas scents the air. She straightens the hankies. I decide too excited is a risk worth taking.

Joanne Nelson is the author of the memoir, *This Is How We Leave.* *wakeupthewriterwithin.com*

An Apartment in February

James didn't know the difference between bleach and ammonia; he grabbed the bottle under his kitchen sink, sprayed a used rag, wiped around the kitchen: this door, the next, inside. *I've never cleaned cupboards*, James thought. He wanted help hanging pictures but didn't know who to ask, much less how.

John Spiegel is an English teacher in Springfield, Ohio and is emotionally attached to his shirts.

Spring Green

It was the color of leaves in April. My mother made it. My brother's wife had a little girl. The note said she'd used the same pattern. I shoved it into a box behind the spare tire. No use Diane finding it, getting upset. I never told you about that?

Melanie Faith likes to wear many professional hats, including as a professor, poet, editor, prose writer, tutor, and photographer. *melaniedfaith.com*

Couples' Friendship Transition

I hug my friend as our husbands hang back outside the restaurant. We're on the waiting list; the bar is closed. I brace myself for sober conversation in the chilly air. We mention things they have in common, like throwing spaghetti at the wall to see if anything sticks.

A special education teacher by day, Theresa Milstein writes middle grade, YA, and dabbles in poetry. *theresamilstein.blogspot.com*

The Muralist

Cool night air sneaked through the bars. When a uniform asked why she vandalized, she stared at cluelessness. *Read headlines,* she mumbled to cinder blocks. Hers: not chaotic calligraphs. Hers: real plastic islands splayed above distraught ocean waves. No need to defend. *Indictments,* she said. The night air agreed.

Carolyn Martin is a lover of gardening and snorkeling, feral cats and backyard birds, writing and photography. *carolynmartinpoet.com*

Saying Goodbye

He'll come crawling back I repeated to myself, before the phone call about my eighty-six-year-old grandmother falling. She told me she hoped my grandfather was praying for her, because "Jack has to be in Heaven by now." Holding her hand, I realized I didn't want my ex, I wanted that.

Lindsay Adams has too many puppets in her apartment and writes essays, flash, and plays in between walking her dog.

On the Morning of the Big Storm

In the brightly lit grocery store, the tall man unloads his shrink-wrapped hot dogs, three kinds of canned cat food, and feather duster onto the counter. Pays with cash. Chokes, *Have a good one,* as he walks wide-eyed out the door.

A lifelong resident of upstate New York, Maryanne Hannan is always in awe of the big impact a few words can make. *mhannan.com*

Fourteen

Under the plum tree I gorged on pomegranate seeds that stained my lips. The alleyway was forbidden, so I pressed my ear against my grandparents' pine fence and listened to the clamor of teenage boys and peeked as they sweated under basketball hoops. I tingled and ate kumquats.

Maria Garcia Teutsch is a poet, editor and professor: *marialoveswords.com*

Men

The guy had to take some of the surrounding breast tissue so I'll be lopsided. And he's like, it won't be a problem. But that's a guy talking, because if he had one ball hanging down, he'd be traumatized.

A journalist by profession, Martha Engber has written hundreds of articles for the *Chicago Tribune* and other national publications. *marthaengber.com*

Uprooted

Sprawling peacefully atop the woodland, my roots unravel and rest. As the hum of the lumberjack's saw draws nearer, they begin to curl. Leather boots appear at my woody trunk. Earthbound I am, and in sawdust strewn; the music of the forest, now off-key, lulls me to sleep.

Debra Danz lives in Switzerland and writes poetry to the clanging of cowbells.

Hit SEND

"Dear He/She/They: I am inquiring whether you have openings in retail, web design, modeling, clowning, cake decorating, traffic control, pediatrics, or plumbing. I possess degrees or certificates in anthropology, oboe, meta-analysis, chicken-sexing, tailoring, and saucepan repair. Hard working, if/when employed." Melinda proofed the email, added "Please, please!" and hit SEND.

Ann S. Epstein writes novels, stories, and memoir and is even shorter than this story. *asewovenwords.com*

Thought Process

I just had a thought. There's another one. And another. They keep coming. I can't stop them. Thought, thought, thought. I can't escape. Thought, thought, thought. I'm helpless. Thought, thought, thought. I'm drowning. Thought, thought, thought. I give up. Thought, thought, thought. I like that one. Thought, thought, thought.

John McCaffrey is a creative writing teacher, columnist, and development director for a large non-profit organization in New York City. *jamccaffrey.com*

Caught by Surprise

Longing to swim, in the molten heat of the sun, she removed her clothes, jumped into the pool, naked, and luxuriated in the water, cool against her skin. 'Glorious morning, Mrs Cadwallader!' Startled, the poolside protecting her modesty, she and the vicar conversed about the flower arranging rota.

Karen Al-Ghabban is a lover of words and languages. Married, two children and a dog.

The Fly

Twenty-four degrees outside; the fly is inside and warm. We become friends. I feed her grapes. She wants more. She wants my apple. She's on my lips. She wants to play. I push her away. Now she's dead on my windowsill. I cannot write. She was my muse.

Steve Zettler is a writer and actor living in Philadelphia, Pennsylvania. His novel, *Careless Love* is published by Vine Leaves Press. *stevezettler.com*

Last Words

"Glad that's over," Will said.
"You gave a too flowery eulogy, Will," Ben said.
"He wrote it himself before he died," Will said. "It's how he wanted the living to remember him."
"I'm just an acquaintance, barely knew him. What part of his life did he leave out?"
"The truth."

Steve Prusky lives and writes in Las Vegas.

I Am

I climb into that place where the moonbeams dance, but the sunlight does not pierce; where my heart sings, but my voice is stilled, and there I listen as the world chunders by. I hear the stillness of peace as it holds my soul. I am me again.

Roland Chesters is a graduate from the University of London, an AIDS Survivor and author of *Ripples from the Edge of Life. silverwoodbooks.co.uk/roland-chesters*

Flew the Coop

My daughter's smooth face contrasts mine on the unforgiving Facetime app. She's surprised me with her new septum piercing. Those first days she called crying daily. Now she bubbles over about her new friends and classes. I nod and smile. And count the days until holiday.

A special education teacher by day, Theresa Milstein writes middle grade, YA, and dabbles in poetry. *theresamilstein.blogspot.com*

(Un)expected

The second time we told no one; we painted my office blue. The third time a colleague brought over a bassinette. I got rid of it before I brought her home. Rolled my desk back. By the fifth, we were three more years in. We no longer spoke trimester, due-date, hope.

Melanie Faith likes to wear many professional hats, including as a professor, poet, editor, prose writer, tutor, and photographer. *melaniedfaith.com*

The Door

The knuckles of the hand gripping the doorknob were white. A deal of force was needed to open the door. Inside was a charnel house with bodies and bits of bodies strewn all over; after sorting them a mystery remained. Where was the arm that matched the hand on the doorknob?

Peter Snell was a bookseller and he wears a lot of red in December. Facebook *@Bartons.Bookshop*

Neon

In the neon shade of the tall gray gallows, she fell to her knees. Her blistered palms grazed the crumbling remains of tiny lives no longer supported by the ruined sun. Nor was hers. Still, she felt compelled to rise and find water. She would mourn later, in the moonlight.

Carolyn R. Russell lives and writes in West Newbury, MA. *carolynrrussell.com*

Drip Drop

Halfway up the close, Janie stopped and reached into the pockets of her dressing gown for something that was no longer there. And then, tightening the cord around her waist, she returned to the deserted street and waited impatiently in the rain for him to come.

Tom Gillespie is a novel and short fiction writer. *tom-gillespie.com*

The Crack House

The crack house two doors down was condemned last week, but one skinny guy in a velour bathrobe putters up to it on his moped, again and again. He knocks and knocks on the door until no one comes. I watch, thinking: *Man, sometimes it's so hard to just let go of things.*

Scott Gould is the author of the novel *Whereabouts*, the memoir *Things That Crash, Things That Fly* from Vine Leaves Press. *scottgouldwriter.com*

Brothers

I wait for Mom and Dad to return from the hospital.
Please wake up.
The rock skips one, two, three times across the calm lake surface before sinking into the deep. It's all in the wrist action. I tried to teach you, like I tried to teach you to swim.

Pushcart nominee, Jayne Martin is also a recipient of Vestal Review's VERA award. Her flash collection, *Tender Cuts*, is published by Vine Leaves Press. *jaynemartin-writer.com*

Oranges

Oranges. Only the juice. Only the juice, sucked, spat out, the sweetness, the dirt, my bike, my altars, praying under the leaves and hanging fruit, my tears, intoxicating blossoms, growing myself up in the orange grove.

Indie Book Award winner, Gleah Powers, has worked as a painter, actor and dancer. Her memoir, *Million Dollar Red*, and novella, *Edna & Luna* are published by Vine Leaves Press. *gleahpowers.com*

Zim-Zoom

Brandon's throat tightened as he glanced away from the sweat pooling in the dip of Laurie's collarbone at the pinprick of light from the webcam. On the screen, nine tiny mouths were agape. A draft chilled his bare upper thighs. To the left of the keyboard his calico, Nala, purred.

The recipient of numerous prizes and grants, Phill Provance's comics, poetry and prose have appeared widely worldwide. *phillprovance.com*

Transformation

My little brother who "knows to keep his mouth shut" writes songs and sings them at the top of his lungs, defying birth order, gender, and parenting, ridiculous and random determinants of personality and power. I am an audience, the big bad bully of a sister crying appreciative tears.

Connie Biewald writes and teaches—and works hard to be kind, which doesn't always come naturally. *conniebiewald.com*

Dead Crow Tonga

Found a dead crow on the welcome mat this morning. Blessed it with a hum and sway of the hips, like a Tonga. Shoveling without touching, the supersized bird glided into a Glad Hefty Bag which I strangled shut. At the bin I wondered: trash or recycle?

Alexis Deutsch-Adler is an artist and a blogger, and she is currently at work on an autofiction novella. *mymuse.typepad.com*

Alfredo

Nicole hated shampooing, so her father convinced Alfredo the Elf to walk on her head while she lathered and rinsed. Alfredo lived in the cellar ducts and wouldn't come out, no matter how Nicole coaxed. He still sends birthday cards signed—in a shakier hand each year—"Your Elf, Alfredo."

John Repp is a poet, fiction writer, and folk photographer living in Erie, Pennsylvania, USA.

Ava Never Wasted Her Bark

I carried the good, old dog, almost sixty pounds still, from the house to the front yard, where she staggered to go pee one last time. Then I lifted her again—this time to the back seat of my pickup truck for the final, fatal trip to the Vet.

D.W. Schmidt lives and writes in Hughson, California, and he misses his dog.

On Being Dealt His Last Hand

Near death, and alone in a twenty-five dollar a week rooming house, Davey Calderone, a grifter, knows he's cheated his last mark. He won't try to cheat Death. Rather, he'll savor his memories of all the places, all the aces, and dearest of all, those beautiful, expectant faces.

Roy Dorman enjoys reading and writing speculative fiction and poetry.

Good Fences Make Good Neighbors

I step out of the house, as if I'm doing something illicit. It's the same fresh air, but without the filter of fabric. *Finally*. My neighbor, walking his Beagle, crosses my path. He's grown a beard flecked with white. I jump back. *Instinct*. We share an uneasy smile.

A special education teacher by day, Theresa Milstein writes middle grade, YA, and dabbles in poetry. *theresamilstein.blogspot.com*

At the Sound of the Beep

He read Mark Strand's poems into my voicemail. Masculine firmness mouthing each word. Susurrus of certain phrases. Over the weeks, he quoted Laughlin, Brautigan, Strand again. His messages were like worms to a baby bird. Beak to beak. I fell from the nest. Then he disconnected and married a roadrunner.

In the wilds of North Texas, Trudi Young Taylor works as a counselor to support her writing habit. *trudiyoungtaylor.com*

A Week Late
Crystal Springs Rhododendron Garden Portland, Oregon

Rhododendrons droop and third graders—field-tripping with their pads and #2s—don't care. They're here to draw what's left: waterfalls, irises, geese. *We can't talk to strangers*, pigtails rebuff my praise of her woodland scene. Some lessons take. Suddenly, goslings appear at lake-edge. My camera prefers fluff to kids.

Previously published in Postcard Poems and Prose Magazine

Carolyn Martin is a lover of gardening and snorkeling, feral cats and backyard birds, writing and photography. *carolynmartinpoet.com*

Flash Psycho

There's movement behind the shower curtain. Adrenalin rockets me from zombie-pee groggy to eyes-on-stalks awake. He steps out, confident. Time slows. His black eyes glitter. Hairs quiver on his legs. I suck in a breath and yell loud enough to wake the dead, "Honey, get a glass."

Byddi Lee is an Irish writer and author of *The Rejuvenation Trilogy* and *March to November* as well as short stories, flash fiction, and plays. *byddilee.com*

Up the Jungle

In snake country I always check my sheets at night and shake out my boots first thing. Yesterday a snake dropped out of my boot and escaped under the bathroom door. It had disappeared so I ran my bath. What do you think came out of the tap? Yup, water.

Peter Snell was a bookseller and he wears a lot of red in December. Facebook *@Bartons.Bookshop*

Covid Days

I forget sometimes. Just go about my business. Writing, petting the dog, scooping ice cream. Immersed. Then the memory wave returns and I calculate every step outside the door's possible cost. Quick review of loved ones, of who's healing and who isn't. Self assessment: Chills? Cough? All day like this.

Joanne Nelson is the author of the memoir, *This Is How We Leave*. *wakeupthewriterwithin.com*

Behind Closed Doors

The light shone from the window, casting a warm glow across the dark landscape. Logs that burned on an open fire, fragranced the air. Jazz played faintly. Walking in the moonlight, the passer-by imagined a happy family, laughing. Inside, the impact of my husband's cold fist sent me to sleep.

Karen Al-Ghabban is a lover of words and languages. Married, two children and a dog.

Test Result

Caller ID flashed her doctor's name. If the test was negative, life would go on as is. If it was positive, everything would change. Either way, could she accept the result? Her life was good, but there were gaps. The test would determine whether she'd have time to fill them.

Ann S. Epstein writes novels, stories, and memoir and is even shorter than this story. *asewovenwords.com*

My Lover's Gun

For Sale: 38 caliber, Smith & Wesson, Model 642 Deluxe revolver. 5 round, aluminum alloy frame (Airweight), double-action, stainless steel cylinder & barrel, rosewood laminate handle & snag-free hammer. Very sexy piece. $250, OBO. Only used once.

Steve Zettler is a writer and actor living in Philadelphia, Pennsylvania. His novel, *Careless Love* is published by Vine Leaves Press. *stevezettler.com*

Upheaval

In the chaos, my heart—the boxes within—they re-ordered themselves. And in the shifting, I caught glimpses of the fire-cracking spectacularism of my internal universe, which I may never see again.

A journalist by profession, Martha Engber has written hundreds of articles for the *Chicago Tribune* and other national publications. *marthaengber.com*

Merry Christmas

The text message says, Meet me in the lot. I don't recognize the number. I look out my kitchen window into the parking lot below. My car is covered in tinsel. My brother nicked it last year, then disappeared. He'd texted, Sorry. He was never good with words.

Jessica Bell is the publisher of Vine Leaves Press. Check out all her other personalities at *iamjessicabell.com*.

Mother

The moment my mother dies, I'm in stirrups having a pap smear. How symbolic is that?

Indie Book Award winner, Gleah Powers, has worked professionally as a painter, actor and dancer. Her memoir, *Million Dollar Red*, and novella, *Edna & Luna* are published by Vine Leaves Press. *gleahpowers.com*

"H"

The needle pierces my worn out vein. A schism between mind and body, thoughts and deeds, widens and I tumble into chaos, search for your eyes in those that turn away. Waves of light bear down on me. Blasts of sound. My head meets the pavement. And there you are.

Pushcart nominee, Jayne Martin, is also a recipient of Vestal Review's VERA award. Her debut flash collection, *Tender Cuts*, is published by Vine Leaves Press. *jaynemartin-writer.com*

Not Chicken

One cock-of-the-walk makes ten hens happy. Two roosters will strut and crow before feathers fly. If the fight is short and one bird dances its wing in a circle around the other, leave them be. The dancer has won and the loser will run, ne'er to crow or mate. Evolution.

Jean Gill is an award-winning writer and photographer living in the south of France. *jeangill.com*

Buff

"You marry?"
"No." I chuckled.
"You have girlfriend?"
"Mm-mm. No polish, just buff please." I replied, trying to change the subject.
"He have three girlfriend!" Giggled an eavesdropper.
Laughter filled the blue neon-lit nail salon, followed by indecipherable chatter then howling hoots.
"I will take polish. Lavender."

Daniel Hart is a 68-year-old hairdresser in Philadelphia who sings country music.

Salt and Seaweed

Salt, seaweed and Coppertone. The intoxicating smells of summer drift in from deep memory. We dig for sand crabs and gather quahog shells. In the shade of a blue striped umbrella, we eat peanut butter sandwiches held in sandy fingers. I hear my mother's laugh. My eyes open to winter.

Barbara is a Philadelphia-based educator, artist and writer.

You're Funny

"You're funny," she said. "I'm a sucker for men with a sense of humor." I didn't care why this goddess bestowed her favors on me; I was ecstatic. This was three years ago. I'm exhausted; amusing her is hard work. I'll introduce her to Malcolm; he's funnier than me.

Michael Fryd is the author of a memoir *My Mother's War*.

Puzzling

We retreat to our corners for work and school. But eventually we gravitate towards the puzzle that has taken over our dining room table. You learn a lot about people by their strategy in those quiet moments of contemplation. When the world outside is falling apart, we build ourselves, piece by piece.

A special education teacher by day, Theresa Milstein writes middle grade, YA, and dabbles in poetry. *theresamilstein.blogspot.com*

Dallas

"I'm coming over," Roger said.
This horrible, dark thing had just happened to us: the convertible, the shots, the elegant wife in pillbox hat flung forward.
My face found Roger's chest. Solace.
The little boy saluted his father as the flag-draped coffin passed.
Six weeks later, I said yes.

Melanie Faith likes to wear many professional hats, including as a professor, poet, editor, prose writer, tutor, and photographer. *melaniedfaith.com*

Riches and Reserves

At the café, Cathy slides sugar packets into her purse. Ellen conveniently forgets her wallet. Josie jots down their next date with a stubby little pencil. The empty shelves still haunt them. The absent flour, yeast, a pork roast. Spring's false promise. Summer's deceit. The smell of privation.

Wisconsin writer Nancy Jorgensen co-authored her 2019 book, Go, Gwen, Go: A Family's Journey to Olympic Gold, with her daughter Elizabeth Jorgensen. nancyjorgensen.weebly.com

On a Dare

It started innocently, with magnifying glasses and smoldering anthills. Then, BB guns and neighborhood weathervanes and the jay on the ridge vent. Menthol Marlboros singeing each other's shoulders, neither flinching. Michelob bottles exploding against century-old headstones. Five-finger discounts and escaping into crosswalks and the sedan, the siren and the shroud.

Rich Gravelin writes flash stories in the precious few moments between central-Maine snowstorms. maineturtle.blogspot.com

Catch of the Day

The fishmonger tightly folds this morning's newspaper around the whole trout for someone's dinner tonight. The crime story in the wrapper doesn't mention that the young mother and the fish died with the same expression—their glassy, black eyes wide open and mouths frozen in an O.

Kate Bradley-Ferrall is a Northern Virginia writer and artist, but not on bodies. Twitter *@KBFerrall*

Father

"He will be back in three days," the resident told us, chart in hand, eyes elsewhere. We saw a different one each day. "Or it might be a week."
We looked at my father in his bed of two weeks, breathing labored, lips dry.
"Or maybe never," my sister snapped.

Emmy-award-winner Amy Bass is a writer, professor, and sport thinker. *amybass.net*

Homo Squirrel

Blood was pouring from his nose as he watched the crowds. His brain was unusual, for a squirrel. His teachers had taught him how they'd grown it from human cells. Yesterday, he'd reached maturity and escaped. Today, despite the bleeding, he couldn't stop scratching his arse and picking his nose.

Stephen Oram's flashfic collections have been praised by publications such as *The Morning Star* and *The Financial Times. stephenoram.net*

Clemency

Decades after the sexual assaults, I came across a dismembered, partially-eaten deer carcass frozen into the shoreline along Lake Michigan. I photographed the crime scene. Raw meat. Shattered bone. Dead cleric yanked from his grave. Wolf tracks circling evidence of my rage. Knees buckling as tears began the thaw.

Kathryn Walczyk is a spiritual companion and a woman claiming her voice. *kathrynwalczyk.weebly.com*

Timing

He sweeps the floor of the aviary with a dustpan and broom; an old jazz drummer shuffling a beat as the canaries provide a counterpoint funereal melody. The seed husks become the collected cacophony of notes he never played. The emptying of his heart. The conductor's baton will soon rest.

Adam Byatt is an English teacher, a writer, a frustrated drummer and a lover of doughnuts. *afullnessinbrevity.wordpress.com*

The Thing They Didn't Take

They took my Toyota. Credit cards. But my sister, Nan, and I told jokes about Adam Sandler, thunderstorms, dictators. We laughed within makeshift fortresses. They sunk my credit scores, called me delinquent instead of scholar. Nan told me to fight. They took the plastic coffee table. I kept the laughter.

Yash Seyedbagheri's work has been published in *The Journal of Compressed Creative Arts*, *Write City Magazine*, and *Ariel Chart*, among others. Twitter *@dudesosad*

Mailman

Mom wrapped the tin in thin paper, topping it with a recycled bow. Put this in the mailbox. Careful—they're expensive. Sometimes he wouldn't get them until January. He'd always leave a thank you. Once, I tried the pretzel shaped cookie dappled with sugar. I didn't see the big deal.

Award-winning author Katherine Gotthardt writes from her Washington D.C. metro home where she plays servant to her two dogs. *katherinegotthardt.com*

Christmas Tree

First house, first full-sized Christmas tree. Every night I get lost in its lights. On Twelfth Night it returns to the top of the car. We travel to the recycling spot. I stand it up, tall and straight once more, among its fallen comrades. I cry as it recedes in the rear-view mirror.

Hannah Poole is a retired university administrator who is active in several ministries at her church in Philadelphia.

You Shouldn't Have Waited This Long

Maxey raised a .38. "Larkin still breathes."
Finn raised palms. "These things take time."
"Every day he's alive feels like pepper in my ass."
Finn sputtered. "The situation wasn't right."
"He paid you off?"
Finn blanched. "No!"
"One of us is superfluous." Maxey sighed. "You shouldn't have waited this long."

Joe Giordano's stories appeared in more than one hundred magazines and has had three novels and a short story collection published. *joe-giordano.com*

Blind Joy

He practiced finding the lube and tissues with his eyes tight shut and he counted the steps between the bathroom and his single bed so he could find the way in the dark. Well, he was a good boy and believed his mother when she said it'd make him blind.

Nettie Thomson is a Scottish writer who is growing her hair. *nettiethomson.com*

A Hole Investigation

Discovering a hole in her case, the detective went to interrogate the subject she previously encountered. The interrogation revealed the subject misheard her ordering doughnuts instead of croissants. He apologized and swapped out the misunderstood order. When she opened the new case, the holes were gone. She closed the case.

Charles Gibson is a writer/editor who lives in Hendersonville, Tennessee and holds an Educational Specialist Degree.

Neighbors

"YOU ARE SO FUCKING ANNOYING!" How does one respond to a note like this, slipped in my mail-slot at 5 a.m. while playing my guitar? True, the walls are thin, and the sound of carnal pursuits I first confused for tormented ghosts wake me at night. I respond. "YOU ARE SO ANNOYING FUCKING!"

Daniel Hart is a 68-year-old hairdresser in Philadelphia who sings country music.

Camping

I don't mind camping.
I don't mind sleeping on hard ground.
I don't mind feet wet from walking in dewy grass.
I don't mind ants in my food.
What I do mind is brushing my teeth in the dark and discovering
that instead of toothpaste I have used insect repellent.

Peter Snell was a bookseller and he wears a lot of red in December. Facebook
@Bartons.Bookshop

The Day After Christmas

Fenders and bike tires are designed to collapse, but bone has little
give. James woke up when the nurse typed on the computer and
then left the room. He didn't recognize the curtains or the bedsheet.
He couldn't move his whatever it was. Metal also remembers little.

John Spiegel is an English teacher in Springfield, Ohio and is emotionally attached
to his shirts.

The Conductor

I see a woman standing at the bus stop, her hands gliding across her cheeks in unison, as if conducting a tiny orchestra. Or fashioning a solo rendition of cat's cradle. Is she tugging on each end of a log saw? No. With great panache she is flossing her teeth.

Houston-based poet Margo Davis says her massive air plant is thriving on The Triplets of Belleville soundtrack.

Summer Days

My friends and I ran through backyard sprinklers. Numbered hopscotch squares on sidewalks, called Red Rover to each other in the alley. We weren't allowed to leave the block. In the evenings, before the streetlights sent us home, we'd sit on the curb at the corner's edge, planning our escape.

Joanne Nelson is the author of the memoir, *This Is How We Leave*. *wakeupthewriterwithin.com*

Watch Out for Human Traffic, It's Bad Today

You can always tell rush hour from the metallic taste of the air— the sharp bite of copper. Also, the dead, bleeding bodies in the streets. Numbers are up. But twenty-thousand Expendables dying in traffic today isn't enough to solve the population problem.

Lindsay Adams has too many puppets in her apartment and writes essays, flash, and plays in between walking her dog.

Heartbeat

Instafixx was nothing but simulations.
Adam couldn't tell the difference between a human or AI influencer anymore.
Enough was enough.
He shut off his phone and fell to the ground—lifeless.

Jess Chua is an award-winning essayist who reads and writes horror stories in her free time. *jesschuabooks.com*

A Whisper Would Be Enough

I wash my hair. It's my mother's exactly. Massaging my scalp, I could be touching hers during the agonizing months before her death, when only my hands felt gentle enough. And here we are, in a world she couldn't possibly fathom. Come back; let us talk. You lived through war.

Cordelia Frances Biddle's Martha Beale series is set in 1840's Philadelphia. *cordeliafrancesbiddle.net*

Dog Down

Yoga, Doc said. Okay, I'll try.
Bend, slowly feeling the body awaken.
Check. Feet flat. Relax into downward dog and hold the pose.
Hold? For how long? Is this supposed to hurt? Connect to Mother Earth? Isn't that gravity's job?
Inhale. Exhale. Rise slowly. Rise.
Rise? A little help here!

Linda Brodsky, pseudonym Lyn Peters, prolific purveyor of the English language.

Arson

Our farm burned. Lost everything. Homeless, but I still have the things that ever did matter. My partner by my side, our children, our love. The right to be liberal heretics in backwoods Kentucky. Hopes still here y'all. It was a gift from alt-right neighbors.

Amanda Jean Alley is a Florida born, Kentucky raised writer, activist, and lover of life. Twitter *@AmandaJeanAlley*

The Heirloom

The heirloom engagement ring she lost in Oregon was found by a traveling Alabama couple who, months later, called the local paper, whose person connected an old "LOST" ad to the find. After which, it was the 1931 inscription that clinched it. That, and the "oh my G-d, it's hers!"

Elli Samuels is a poet and cookbook author who grew up in a cozy East Coast town, spent decades in Texas, and now lives in the Pacific Northwest.

Take My Hand

"Strokes do strange things to people," said the ambulance driver, when asked about Dorothy slapping the waiter before she collapsed. When really, she was reaching for her Joe, her handsome Joe in his uniform, who was saying, "I'm itching to see you, Dot."

Cheryl Lawton Malone is a freelance writer, creative consultant, and award-winning poet with two published picture books. *cheryllawtonmalone.com*

Before

your brother was diagnosed with cancer, before the crazy woman moved into the fishing cabin and brown earth with stubbles of dried grass stuck out like the hairs of a balding man ... before the orange sun shuddered in a harp of light; before that, I loved you.

Lenore Weiss lives in Oakland, California where she tutors middle- and high-school students in writing.

Venus Descending

"One lousy unicorn. God, that hurt."
Forehead damp; the needle made her sweat.
A clunky pirouette off the table to the mirror—a Degas ballerina.
Eyes bulging, seeing, not believing, she crumpled to the floor. Her
lovely back's canvas exposed my revenge—the custard swirl of
dogshit beneath swarming flies.

Robb White is a Midwestern writer of hardboiled novels and genre fiction.
tomhaftmann.wixsite.com/robbtwhite

Hired Killer

"I brought you where we can't be disturbed to revise the plan to
kill your wife."
"Whatever, but I'm not paying the second half until she's dead."
"No problem, I'm satisfied with your advance, but she paid more."
Bang

Doug Hawley is a little old man who lives with editor and cat in Lake Oswego
Oregon USA. *doug.car.blog*

Double

As a going away present, your driver received pepper spray with a retractable sharp edge on the handle. She's only ever used it once, to cut open candy letters and spell happy birthday on a double chocolate cake, but still keeps it in the glove compartment. Just in reach.

Kirby Wilson is a senior at the SC Governor's School for the Arts & Humanities who often wears white. Instagram *@kirbyljwilson*

Mood Music

Lips stiff, he kissed me as I entered, doorbell still resonating. He handed me a drink. We settled on the couch, legs touching. After Formula One and football replays, he cued mood music, adjusting gauzy 4-poster curtains. After, I went home, cold as stars. I didn't know he had Asperger's.

Rebecca Rothenberg, a writer, editor, and consultant, is also a Forest Landscape Ecologist.

Mrs. Krouse

Our white-haired landlady crept above our flat, swept the creaky stairs, her accent thick as my mother's black bread spread with limburger cheese. Once, I saw her float down the stairs into the basement, her angel wings carrying her to the old country of broken-down washing machines.

Sherri Levine is a poet and a fiction writer living in Portland, Oregon. *sherrilevine.com*

Rough Justice

Newly divorced, I decided to finance my next vacation by selling my engagement ring. The store's owner flirted and fenced with me before agreeing to pay my asking price. "You know," he smiled, "I don't usually buy stones this small."
"Next time," I smiled, "I'll try to do better."

Jan Bartelli is a former journalist, a more-or-less retired attorney and a less-is-more writer of creative non-fiction.

Haircut

We never embrace nor touch. Sometimes, we share a beer. When he mentioned he needed a haircut, I offered. My father's hair was softer than I imagined. It was a beautiful mix of red, white and gray. I lingered behind him, holding his head in my hands. He waited patiently.

Lindsay Erdman is a Visual Arts educator, artist, writer and musician based in Toronto, Canada. *lindsayerdman.net*

Fingernails

One-two-three-four-five-six, blow. One-two-three-four-five-six, blow. The same rhythm every time. Each rasp of her emery board makes me grip the steering wheel tighter. At arm's length she studies her work, spots a flaw and attacks the inexactitude in cadence. She splays five fingers, nods and begins the other hand. One-two-three-four-five-six, blow.

DL Shirey's work has appeared in 60 journals, including *Confingo*, *Page & Spine*, *Zetetic* and *Wild Musette*. *dlshirey.com*

Traveler

She came into the library weekly. Graying hair, a long, dark coat. Mute, she stared at the world globe, held it as if embracing a loved one. Her face near weeping. When approached, she stormed out. Was she trying to find her way home? I hope she found it.

Susan Moorhead is a poet and writer and ardent snapshot-taker living in New York.

Accident?

How utterly absurd, to die this way, amid soapy suds and dish-water, the slipped wine glass in bits in the sink, one slim sliver protruding from an artery in her wrist, the artery pumping like a tiny scarlet fountain, her left hand a spectator, unmoved, not wanting to get involved.

Paul Negri, who lives in New Jersey, is a fairly short writer of short pieces whose work has appeared in more than 50 publications. *faulknersociety.org/paul-negri-author*

Highway Lotto

Freeway driving at midnight: Dead buck dead ahead, Mack truck to the right. Seventy mph over the deer, went flying. Still coming down.

Catherine Parnell is a Boston-based writer and editor with Birch Bark Editing. *catherineparnell.com*

On the Way to the Show

Donna couldn't bear to see the dog shivering in NYC snow, a homeless woman covering him with her body, a shield. Donna was supposed to see a play. Instead, she turned around, walked nine blocks to Petsmart. She guessed on sweater and blanket size. It never felt like enough.

Katie Darby Mullins is a professor and writer. She is also the executive writer and a producer of the Underwater Sunshine Festival. Twitter *@katieUWSF*

Carnival Summer

On the hot, dusty day, I call people over to the balloon-dart game, although it's out of my introvert comfort zone. Their faces light up when they win. Until they see the hairy slug. "Play again for a chance to win a bigger prize." At home, I wash the grime from my skin.

A special education teacher by day, Theresa Milstein writes middle grade, YA, and dabbles in poetry. *theresamilstein.blogspot.com*

The End of the Road

Heat baked off the tarmac in the late afternoon making Jameson sweat in the seat of his ancient car. The glare burned his eyes as he headed west, aiming for home by nightfall; failing to spot the basking lizard or feel a bump as the suspension absorbed the shock.

Peter Snell was a bookseller and he wears a lot of red in December. Facebook *@Bartons.Bookshop*

Dead Men Don't Eat Crow

On stage, in my youth, I played Camus' Caligula. "Those we have killed are always with us. But they are no great trouble." Caligula died at 29, Camus at 46. If only they had camped out long enough to know the truth.

Steve Zettler is a writer and actor living in Philadelphia, Pennsylvania. His novel, *Careless Love* is published by Vine Leaves Press. *stevezettler.com*

Fido's Lament

He thinks he's funny. He begs, "Fido, grind the coffee beans?" He's sure he's clever. "Fidorable, mix me a martini?" He's convinced he's cute. "Fidopteris, the blue shirt or the green?" I'm a dog, dunderhead. Not a valet. I lack opposable thumbs. I'm color blind. Ask me how you smell.

Ann S. Epstein writes novels, stories, and memoir and is even shorter than this story. *asewovenwords.com*

Chastened

We arrived too late, after hitching a lift back from a lake. Let's just climb the fence, I said. In darkness, we scaled the 8-footer, away from the guarded entrance. Next morning, at breakfast, we joked about our bravado, until someone said, Here, we shoot first, ask questions later.

Karen Al-Ghabban is a lover of words and languages. Married, two children and a dog.

Night Shift at the Final Stop Café

Quarter of four and he orders the last piece of coconut cream pie. Not the freshest I say, but he says he don't mind. He drops a dime into the tabletop juke. Johnny Mathis croons "Chances Are." He asks me to dance. My swollen, bare feet follow his out the door into the dawn.

Pushcart nominee, Jayne Martin is also a recipient of Vestal Review's VERA award. Her debut flash collection, *Tender Cuts*, is published by Vine Leaves Press. *jaynemartin-writer.com*

The Gift

With solemnity and pride her slack jaw drops the deadest of dead at my feet. There is no skin, no feathers, no beak. Only a tight network of fine cold bones meant to take flight. Perhaps what once was someone else's meal, someone else's baby too is today's gift to me.

Alexis Deutsch-Adler is an artist and blogger currently at work on an auto-bio fiction novella. *mymuse.typepad.com*

The Question

Nerves tighter and tighter. Can't sleep. Lose weight. Then, opportunity comes, in the hall between classes. I stop him with a word. Stammer gulp stammer uh, Billy would you go to the prom with me? No. Crushed, melted into a puddle. How can I continue on?

Hannah Poole is a retired university administrator who is active in several ministries at her church in Philadelphia.

Letters

She carried the box into the backyard, past the bird feeders to the place of last resort. Stepping up to the rusty barrel, she took a breath. Yellowed letters placed deep within built a nest. A match was struck. The flame grew. Tears dried. A swell of calm overcame her.

Barbara is a Philadelphia-based educator, artist and writer.

The Holy Trinity

"Son, there're only three things that made the last five years tolerable." Tears filled my eyes as I glanced at the photo of our beautiful kids that Marianne had just placed next to Dad's hospice bed. "Yup. Metamucil, Viagra and Pot Gummies, the holy trinity."

Daniel Hart is a 68-year-old hairdresser in Philadelphia who sings country music.

A Woman Walks Alone in the Dark

Shadows lengthen into monsters along the alley walls but this is her way home from work. Behind her, footsteps clickety-clack. Man shoes. Newspapers say he's out there. Don't walk alone, ladies. *Clickety-click*, faster, nearer. Nowhere to go. Pretend it's nothing. Heart pounding. "Boo!" Her work-mate laughs. She could kill him.

Jean Gill is an award-winning writer and photographer living in the south of France. *jeangill.com*

You Are My Beloved

I watch you. You eye me, then come closer, the move surprisingly awkward considering your customary grace. I smile. I yearn to speak. I would reach out a hand in friendship, but sense the gesture might alarm you. A hawk in my small, city garden. How wondrous is life.

Cordelia Frances Biddle's Martha Beale series is set in 1840's Philadelphia. *cordeliafrancesbiddle.net*

The Best Hair Cut

My husband went to my parents. Forgetting he was there, my mother cut father's hair. Them married 40 years. Done, she offered to suck him off. My husband thought about jumping out the window to his death. My father declined. But she insisted, "The vacuum is just in the hall."

Amanda Jean Alley is a Florida born, Kentucky raised writer, activist, and lover of life. Twitter *@AmandaJeanAlley*

Myth

A bunch of them broke into my home shouting gibberish while I was sleeping. I tried to get them to leave, but they pointed odd looking weapons at me. I had no choice but to fire my lasers at them. Until now, I thought humans were a myth.

Doug Hawley is a little old man who lives with editor and cat in Lake Oswego Oregon USA. *doug.car.blog*

Music Store

During break, the musicians hung out at the register. The twins taught lessons—a trumpeter and a saxophonist. The trumpet player dated the violinist who looked like a model. Until she cheated on him. Sax players always get the girls. I, like a bartender, listened to the trumpet player's heartbreak.

A special education teacher by day, Theresa Milstein writes middle grade, YA, and dabbles in poetry. *theresamilstein.blogspot.com*

The Magpie

Poor thing has lost all its tail feathers said Melissa as she watched the magpie strut like an ungainly duck. Over weeks it got used to hand feeding and sometimes brought shiny pebble gifts. Melissa was grumpy, then overjoyed, the day it brought the diamond missing from her engagement ring.

Peter Snell was a bookseller and he wears a lot of red in December. Facebook *@Bartons.Bookshop*

Four Oh

Every day, Jessica Bell, Publisher of Vine Leaves Press, reads through the 50 Give or Take submissions, and spends hours scheduling emails so that they arrive in your inbox, like clockwork, at the same time every day. Jessica has a toddler who's 17 months old and enjoys speaking about herself in third person. Today is Jessica Bell's birthday. She has turned the big FOUR Oh. What are you going to do about it? For starters, you are going to forgive her for making you read 90 words instead of 50.

Jessica Bell is the publisher of Vine Leaves Press. Check out all her other personalities at *iamjessicabell.com.*

Further Away

Papa is on his way to the hospital—again. Watching the ambulance lights flash, then fade from view, I whisper, *please keep breathing.* Those words thicken the pulp of my thoughts; put distance between us. Beyond the lonesome, blaring siren, I hear the highway moving— while I stand dead still.

Debra Danz lives in Switzerland and writes poetry to the clanging of cowbells.

The Doctor-Patient Relationship

It was late when she called him, asking if he had something for a broken heart. She'd remembered his sweet bedside manner out behind the garage where they'd played "doctor" at age five. She laughed and felt better when he told her to take some aspirin and call him in the morning.

Roy Dorman enjoys reading and writing speculative fiction and poetry.

The Heart Attack

Cannula in back of each fist. Oxygen monitor taped to a finger. Blood pressure cuff round an arm, inflating every thirty minutes. Electrodes stuck all over me wired to a machine beeping every 20 seconds. When it stops, I wonder am I flatlining? Nobody seems bothered. They're looking after me.

Roland Chesters is a graduate from the University of London, an AIDS Survivor and author of Ripples from the Edge of Life. *silverwoodbooks.co.uk/roland-chesters*

If only...

She squats. In the High Street. I'm frazzled, no mood to coax. I count aloud. I turn and walk on; her brother always followed. But she has my nature. I look back and see her running away, fast. I follow. Bang. Metal crushing. Frightened screams. My heart sinks.

Karen Al-Ghabban is a lover of words and languages. Married, two children and a dog.

That Hound

That hound always wanted out. Didn't mind cold, wet, winds fit to take down trees. And never barked 'cept at deer trying a shortcut. So we'd never heard nothing like the one, clipped howl that frigid night and then his tie-out cut clean through and not a spot of blood.

Chet Ensign writes in northern New Jersey, inventing things that live beyond the outdoor lights.

Good Fences

He woke and saw corpses in the coop. "Dammit, Clem!" He picked up his Colt and barged out. They needed a brick wall. Chain link was weak. Dead roosters were fine ... but hens? No point shooting the dog. But Clem? Start with those tires on that new Ram.

Kael Moffat works as an academic librarian. He loves kayaking, playing drums, and taking photographs. *kmoffatwork.wixsite.com/wasichuchronicles*

Iggie the Writer

November ate all the leaves. Iggie loved his words. His novel. Its impact. Remy channeled Iggie's energy and peed on everything. In sync. In spirit. Dogs know. "I'm so happy we found each other," his prospective agent would remark. They'd be in sync too. His dog, his agent, and Iggie.

Elaina Battista-Parsons is a novelist from New Jersey who loves to write about writers. *elainawrites.com*

The Tallest Tree

You make your hands into stairs and we climb to the very top. Free of the ground's reach, we become ourselves again, the only things alive above the clouds. Every morning, we'll watch the rainbows untie themselves, waiting for the rain.

Kate LaDew is a graduate from the University of North Carolina at Greensboro with a BA in Studio Art.

Virtue

She wanted to slam the screaming baby into the wall. Instead, she walked outside, where the wails diminished, and she rocked. When frustration yielded to duty, she returned to soothe the baby. Later, she heard a woman had drowned her children. She tried to display a look of uncomprehending horror.

Allene Nichols lives in Mississippi, where she writes, teaches, and takes photographs. *allenen.wordpress.com*

The Student

We recommended her for the research grant. "You really like me!" she exclaimed, surprised. We didn't. Instead, we celebrated when she headed for the village from which no anthropologist had returned alive. She came back with a prize-winning ethnography. We should have known: Not even the cannibals could stomach her.

Diane Lefer chose to be a writer rather than an anthropologist but still works with people worldwide. *dianelefer.weebly.com*

Ownership

Spent his last five grand on an acre tract of loblolly pines with an abandoned strip of two-lane asphalt running down the middle. Liked to park there at dusk and do whatever made him feel safe: listen to the mourning doves coming to roost, nap ... pee on the center line.

Scott Gould is the author of the novel *Whereabouts*, the memoir *Things That Crash, Things That Fly* from Vine Leaves Press. *scottgouldwriter.com*

The Reason Why

Her mother was her sister. That's how come she done it. That's what Pa said. "How come she done it?" I asked. "'Cause her mother was her sister," Pa said. "That's how come." I sat on the river's bank watchin' the current. And dusk spread its pall far and wide.

Michael Howard's essays and short stories have appeared in a variety of print and digital publications. *michaelwilliamhoward.com*

Lucky 13

Bingo night. Ladies play with lucky trinkets surrounding their cards. Beside me, a woman strokes her finger along a four-leaf clover. All I've got are thirteen stitches and a bruise shaped like Nebraska. I win multiple jackpots; rake in enough cash for fine wine and steak at The Majestic Fork.

Lisa Marie Lopez resides in Northern California and has had fiction recently published in *Blink-Ink* and *The Ocotillo Review*. Facebook *@authorlisamariefiction*

Curved Roads

Curved country roads with no division lines seem gentler than their highway brethren. Flowing through fields like gray asphalt ribbons, I navigate with trepidation, slowing instead of zooming, because, for all their beauty, I fear what might appear from behind those curves from where I cannot see.

Joan Leotta plays with words on page and stage. *joanleotta.wordpress.com*

The Mark

I nearly hit his car as we pulled into adjacent parking spaces. Angry, I ran up to him. He stayed in his seat. "I was distracted by your bumper sticker. Why does it read 26.1?" At last he spoke: "I only know that I always fall short of the mark."

Clyde Liffey lives near the water. Twitter *@clydeliffey*

Tonight

Will the roses on the table even get noticed? She touched up her makeup, hoping her perfume wasn't too overpowering. With butterflies in her stomach, she threw a quick glance around the bedroom. Everything looked in place. Anticipation built up. Her foster children were coming home.

Radhika Baruah is a bookworm experimenting with wordplay. *beingmeema.wordpress.com*

Old Days

He remembered me from the old days. He asked about buying. It's easier to say no than to explain. I'm tired of showing off the colostomy bag.

Kate E Lore splits her time between a graphic and written memoir, screen plays, flash, comics, and her dating blog. *kateelore.com*

Affixation

We pressed together for heat, watching the riders pass: blue wool, lit by the flame of a pipe. Vgido began to cry and I grasped her mouth, palm tight against her face. One rider paused, hunting the dark. Our breath faded as I stared into a pale teen face.

M. A. Dubbs is an award-winning LGBT Mexican-American poet from the Hoosier state. *melindadubbs.wordpress.com*

Window Seat

The yard was barely big enough for the dog and kids to run around; the kitchen was outdated; the bathroom tiles were cracked. But from the bedroom window seat, she could watch as sunrise lifted her hopes and moonrise illuminated her dreams. She texted the realtor and made an offer.

Ann S. Epstein writes novels, stories, and memoir and is even shorter than this story. *asewovenwords.com*

Field of Bags

Winter's dusk: a row of dormant vines tied to rusted t-bars soldier up, erect, waiting for Spring's orders. A hundred yards away, aged and shorn, brittle and broken, bundled vines sack under white plastic tarps before transport to the burn. In the dimming light they are monster body bags in the field.

Alexis Deutsch-Adler is an artist and blogger currently at work on an auto-bio fiction novella. *mymuse.typepad.com*

Nerve-ana

"You can't imagine how happy it makes me to hear you finally say that." I'd never seen my therapist more elated. I merely mentioned I was considering meditation. Why the big deal? So I asked, "Why are you so happy I'm considering meditation?" He seemed confused. "Meditation? I thought you said medication."

Daniel Hart is a 68-year-old hairdresser in Philadelphia who sings country music.

An Agitation of Bees in Springtime

Now! We're swarming! Seeking a new home. Workers and drones all flying together and in the heart of the swarm, protected by her cadre of bodyguards, the queen, exuding the scent that united them and gave them purpose. Leaving the old hive to a daughter and braving the unknown.

Jean Gill is an award-winning writer and photographer living in the south of France. *jeangill.com*

Spin Cycle

Midnight shift at the laundromat and I replay "Summer Wind" for Arthur. He's a regular; frayed waistcoat, bowtie, baggies of quarters labeled by state.
"Where to tonight, Artie?"
"Maine. My Rose loved tangos along the coast."
Arthur whirls a threadbare dress past the dryers, empty Ziplocs waltz in their wake.

Rich Gravelin writes flash stories in the precious few moments between central-Maine snowstorms. *maineturtle.blogspot.com*

Get Well

Each Monday morning, he finds a new address on Google and mails a stranger a get well card. He likes the ones in lavender envelopes. "Feel better soon" is how he signs the inside, but never adds his name. Never a return address. He guesses everybody is sick of something.

Scott Gould is the author of the novel *Whereabouts*, the memoir *Things That Crash, Things That Fly* from Vine Leaves Press. *scottgouldwriter.com*

A Delightful Delay

Angie sprinted through the shimmering door. Fairies descended and led her, laughing, into merry dance. Many songs later, Angie's new friends returned the exhausted mortal to her own time and place. Puzzled to find Angie sleeping in the alley he'd just chased her into, the assassin shrugged. Money was money.

Alison McBain is an award-winning author, editor, and scribbler of comics about motherhood. *alisonmcbain.com*

A Sudden Death

Mrs Beaton had researched what death would cause Floyd the most suffering. Nerve agents and poisons were too slow and subtle, and Amazon didn't stock them anyway. She wanted something shocking and certain. So, as the waiter served coffee at their fiftieth anniversary dinner, she shot herself in the head.

Avery Mathers keeps bees and monitors moths in the Scottish Highlands, but mostly he writes. *averymathers.com*

Dance

He owned the dance floor, his confidence bordering on cockiness. Yet she accepted his invitation without hesitation. Their bodies moved in sync, until her stiletto heel betrayed her. Before she could object, she was in his car, headed for the ER. But wasn't the hospital in the other direction?

Darcy Grabenstein is a content marketer transplanted from the Florida Panhandle to the Philly 'burbs. *thehiredhandink.com*

Pictures of You

I scour the internet, listening to every punk-rock song, hunting the one you dedicated to me. I was lost in the dark, lost in a sea of strangers, lost in you. *Why do all of The Cure's songs feel the same?* Makes it difficult to find my song. And you.

Jass Aujla plans perfect (fictional) murders during her boring day-job meetings. *jassaujla.com*

In the End

You lost a promotion, a client, your erection. Our singlewide lists mired, rusting, rain-soaked and mildewed, sofa springs sprung, cable disconnected. We stopped having sex. You never wrote your novel, *The History of Something*, or you wrote a condensed version and forgot it on the subway.

Dale Champlin is a poet from Oregon who writes short stuff in long-hand. *champlindesign.com*

Granny

She remembers being a girl in Kashmir. And her childhood pet cow, Lakshmi. And being a newlywed. And the recipe for killer mango *achar*. But she doesn't remember us. She thinks we're nice strangers, and always reacts with wonder to see us ... not realizing we wouldn't exist but for her.

Susmita Ramani lives in the San Francisco Bay Area, weaving worlds and embedding jewel-like people. Twitter *@susmitabythebay*

Lost

I looked at the squirrel and wondered if I could eat it raw. I don't know how to start a fire and probably couldn't catch it anyhow. My wife, what's her name, always threatened to abandon me in the woods when I became demented, but I didn't believe it.

Doug Hawley is a little old man who lives with editor and cat in Lake Oswego Oregon USA. *doug.car.blog*

There They Were

There they were. My mother was a terrible cook. We all rebelled. My sister faked illness to avoid dinner, my brother put them in his pocket, and I closed my eyes and swallowed. Thirty years later looking into an Ikea freezer, I shuddered, closed my eyes, and hurried by … Swedish meatballs.

Rosanne Ehrlich is a writer/producer in the entertainment industry and has pieces in *Chicken Soup for the Soul* and *Persimmon Tree.*

Cliché

I know I sound cynical, but I've worked here for so long it's hard to see beyond the couples bickering over stale coffee, the same three songs playing endlessly on the juke. And yet, I'm still waiting for my own fight. My own stale coffee. Maybe I'm just a cliché.

Mary Pritchard is a writer and content strategist living in Chicago and working on her first novel. *marysheilapritchard.com*

Name and Place

Marcus's bloody bag hides an impervious envelope. Tucked inside is a sterile, single-use-only, human soul, or so he says. When he dies, quietly it'll slip away—returned to its creator, or so he says. The manufacturer's name and place is displayed on the envelope, if we could find it.

Katherine Shehadeh is a writer, mom, student and disgruntled attorney, in an ever-shuffling order. *katherinesarts.com*

Winter

Dawn's fingers had barely reached the cold, blue winter horizon. My senses were stirring. I listened to the puff, puff breaths of my partner still deep in warming slumber. Instinctively, icy toes wriggled across the bottom of the bed. As they found their mark I sighed, "Ah! Perquisites of matrimony."

A Jersey Girl at heart, Barbara Elliott lives, paints and writes in Philadelphia.

The 50-Word Story

The level of angst-ridden doubt, triggered by the need to write a fifty-word story, led to extended ruminating, so much so that, by the time the laptop had sprung awake, the life-affirming water gurgling warmly through gritty coffee grounds had made far greater creative progress than any written word.

Kate Noble aims to produce a unique experience 'waking up' the mind whilst touching the soul.

Too Old for Grievances

Regrets. When you voted Della off the cheerleader's squad. Told her she was priggish. Said her daughter hated her. Anger. When Della tattled you stole the apple. Told the seventh-grade boys your bra was padded. Seduced your husband. But old friends grow sparse. You still remember Della's number. You dial.

Ann S. Epstein writes novels, stories, and memoir and is even shorter than this story. *asewovenwords.com*

Snow

The TV weatherman was making a far bigger deal about the snow than needed. Bundled up, he knelt with a ruler. "A little under three inches with a light crust on top." My mind drifted to LiJun, the handsome Chinese exchange student who gave me gonorrhea in 1981.

Daniel Hart is a 68-year-old hairdresser in Philadelphia who sings country music.

Unfounded Worry

When passing the bathroom, she spotted her 5-year-old son peeing. He stood at the toilet, his back to her, unaware of her presence. It worried her, how serious he could be. When he finished, he plucked a tissue from a box on the back of the toilet. Wiping himself, he said, "Achoo."

A journalist by profession, Martha Engber has written hundreds of articles for the *Chicago Tribune* and other national publications. *marthaengber.com*

Siblings

Phone rings. My sister. Jesus, now what? Probably calling from the NYPD sub-station. How much this time? I'm so fucking sick of this shit. I scream at the phone, "Get your fucking act together." I answer it. "Mr. Zettler, this is Dr. Anderson. I'm with the New York City morgue."

Steve Zettler is a writer and actor living in Philadelphia, Pennsylvania. His novel, *Careless Love* is published by Vine Leaves Press. *stevezettler.com*

Graduation Day

Hot summer day at the Royal Albert Hall. Day of a national transport strike. Ceremony over, still wearing my gown, I run down the streets to hail a passing taxi. "Quick, to Westminster Abbey!" I gasp. "Any friend of Batman's is a friend of mine!" he replies. "Hop in!"

Roland Chesters is a graduate from the University of London, an AIDS Survivor and author of *Ripples from the Edge of Life. silverwoodbooks.co.uk / roland-chesters*

Disconnect

Adored, cosseted, I perch upon the long, zinc-topped table watching the scrubbing and drying of dishes. Laughter and sunlight abound. I'm eight. I sing a song, smile to a smiling world. On the way home, my parents' car lurches, the reek of rage and booze engulfs me. Some moments linger.

Cordelia Frances Biddle's Martha Beale series is set in 1840's Philadelphia. *cordeliafrancesbiddle.net*

At Cape St. Vincent

Giant slabs of rock sit atop the sea like boxes on a table, two hundred feet high. It seemed so much higher when you were here with me, kicking rocks off the edge of the world. I never heard a splash. I just turned and you were gone.

Mike Herndon is a former journalist and current adjunct instructor whose fiction has appeared in numerous publications. Twitter *@TheMikeHerndon*.

Little Miss

"Tuffet" sounded softer than it felt. I settled, tucked my legs.
"Pretty as a picture," the director said. He handed me a bowl of goo.
I was supposed to eat this? A tech adjusted the lights.
"Shooting in five." Then, "Smile!"
But when those eight hairy legs appeared, I screamed.

Erin Dionne writes novels and picture books for kids, flash fiction for adults, and lives outside of Boston with her husband, two children, and a disgruntled dog. *erindionne.com*

I Am

I am terrible at suppressing emotions, except in a relationship.

Richard LeBlond is a retired biologist and active writer and photographer still alive in North Carolina.

My Rapist's Heart

Kelly relives her rape every night; the only difference now is that she is witnessing the scene from the rapist's point of view. Every day she wakes up confused between raw excitement and engulfing emptiness.

Arch Delaro is looking for his first graphic novel collaboration | Product designer working for musicians. Twitter *@landrmusic*

The Painter

While the painter worked, a feral feline chased a terrified squirrel across his pan of paint, their bodies soaked in scarlet. Fur and red pigment flew as they desperately fought on his drop cloth. The painter framed this stained canvas, submitted it to an art show, and won first prize.

Steve Bailey is a retired schoolteacher who lives in Richmond, Virginia, and is starting a second career as a freelance writer. *vamarcopolo.blogspot.com*

One Voice

Glass shattered. My ears buzzed. Feet pounded across the floor. Voices murmured like a dull roar. Fluorescent light blurred my vision. Bodies milled in every direction. One voice cut through the din. "Write your name on the board." Dropping dishes was a crime these days.

Ashley Smith is an emerging writer with a few published pieces.

The Last Biscuit

She patted out the biscuit dough, imagining him splitting the warm biscuit and slathering it with butter and jam. He'd take the first bite and then, later, double over as his stomach twisted and cramped. He really shouldn't have slept with her best friend. Well, that won't ever happen again.

Sarah Scott is a chef in the wine country of Northern California who writes about food and and growing up in the South. *sarahscottchef.com*

First Day

That first day of school, her stomach sunk, a pale unknown. The child searched for her name between the anonymous rows and found it under a peg. The moment stuck in her psyche as she grew; the narrative of plenty and loss trapped under her skin, flexing and tightening.

Jenny Dunbar is a writer and potter.

The March Wind

The March wind caught my ballcap and I gave chase, activating the pups' sense of fun. At 82 my running looks scarecrow-crazy, stooping and snatching, the pups leaping to lick my face. All were laughing at ballcap capture, me, pups, cap, wind. I was the only one out of breath.

Guinotte Wise welds steel sculpture and writes on a farm in Resume Speed, Kansas. *wisesculpture.com*

Live Comedy

The show's late but my mother insists on coming. Within the audience of eight, she nestles into the front row and is asleep and snoring gently before I'm onstage. I do fine. When I wake her up after, she announces I was hilarious ... says she was just resting her eyes.

Justin Terry drinks coffee, listens to YouTube videos of rain, and collaborates with his brilliant poetic friends. Instagram *@justinthewalls*

Simple Pleasures

Pounding snow covers the sidewalk. Wind blurs my eyes. The storefronts dark on the street till I bathe in the light of the liquor store. Smiling while holding the six-pack and heading back.

Tom Keating is working on his 2nd memoir, a story of his adjustment to civilian life after the war.

Party of Five, Please

Five turkey vultures are circling the yard, poking their cruel, red beaks into my newly green March lawn. I'm told a child has gone missing in this small, New England town.

Jan Bartelli is a former journalist, a more-or-less retired attorney and a less-is-more writer of creative non-fiction.

First Night

Far flung into blissful unfamiliarity, she had arrived at her new destination. Her feet floated as she inhaled the hot night air. Bright halogen lamps bounced off her unshowered skin, and a giddiness beamed from within her. It was as if she knew exactly what was going to happen next.

Lindsay Erdman is a Visual Arts educator, artist, writer and musician based in Toronto, Canada. *lindsayerdman.net*

Liver Baby

You held your own liver, cradling it like some dark baby that had chosen you to give it birth. You cooed, stroked it, the silky skin a surprise. It did not wiggle; it had no mouth to smile. And yet somehow you were certain it was happy in your arms.

Chet Ensign writes in northern New Jersey, inventing things that live beyond the outdoor lights.

Estranged

When her husband complained he had gone months without sex, she grew silent. The mother she hadn't seen in 27 years had just left their apartment. Realizing his selfishness, he too grew silent, then berated himself. She didn't disagree. Years went by. Her husband and kids left. Her mother returned.

Jennifer A. Minotti is a Writer-in-Residence at the Center for Women's Health and Human Rights and the founder of the *Journal of Expressive Writing*. journalofexpressivewriting.com

The Volunteer

"Scholar? He was a goddamned volunteer, or were you too busy looking into his dreamy brown eyes to notice the gigantic badge dangling around his neck?" Visiting the Liberty Bell had taken its toll on Tim. Miranda furrowed her brow. "You thought brown?" she asked. "Was thinking more deep hazel."

Daniel Hart is a 68-year-old hairdresser in Philadelphia who sings country music.

Lacy Inspiration

Late for another appointment, the model left the artist's studio in a hurry, leaving her lacy, lime-green bra under the bed where it had strayed. In doing so, she had unwittingly given the muse of the painter's wife the idea for what turned out to be a poetic gem.

Roy Dorman enjoys reading and writing speculative fiction and poetry.

The New Math

If a total of eight people are shot to death at three massage parlors in Atlanta, Georgia, and the following week 10 people are shot to death at a supermarket in Boulder, Colorado, how long before the next mass shooting occurs? Show all work.

Howie Good's most recent poetry collection is Gunmetal Sky, available from Thirty West Publishing.

Spring Rain

I walked the roadside, face bowed, dismal. When the first drops hit, I left my hood down and let the rain dampen my hair. Its wet, warm fingers rolled over my scalp. My neck and shoulders relaxed, the rain increasing. Then I smelled the earth freshen, my sadness washing away.

Norbert Kovacs lives and writes in Hartford, Connecticut. *norbertkovacs.net*

Poor Gerald

After seeing The Godfather, Gerald Giparino knew what he wanted to be. But he was timid. Broke into a bank once. But it was a piggy bank. He had dreadful vision. Gerald wished to be a tough guy. But the only thing the feds wanted him for was jury duty.

Michael Drezin, a lawyer in the Bronx, is working on a collection of short stories.

The Walk

The hallway didn't look that long, but now it felt like miles. Feet stumbling forgetting how to work. Always ahead of himself. Like the juice was already in his veins. The door loomed before him growing with each step. A big hungry mouth. That cell so far behind him now.

Kate E Lore splits her time between a graphic and written memoir, screen plays, flash, comics, and her dating blog. *kateelore.com*

Love Note

Our love is like the old Post-It note covered in gibberish that meant something to me at the time. But now it seems so cryptic I no longer know what.

Jessica Needle is a naturopathic doctor in Palm Desert, California, who dreams of becoming the next William Carlos Williams.

Perspective

Posters plastered the front windows of the convenience store, promising a hefty and continuously growing reward for information on the latest infamous act of animal cruelty. Josh stalked from the store, incoherent with rage and pain. Yet another refused to accept a poster for yet another missing child. His child.

A retired teacher, Martha Sherman now writes and works on her photography, when her very demanding cat allows her to do so.

Marauder

He marauds the nest of small blue eggs, nestled in the cherry tree, then flies, treasure in beak, to the ground. Another crow, racing on foot to the action, watches its peer consume its prize. Later, Robin returns to her nest, unaware of crows, now gone. I guess robins don't know how to count.

Susan R. Barclay is a writer and educator, who enjoys the simple things in life. Twitter @susanrbarclay

Hawaii

Hawaii kills a dozen tourists every year. Middle-aged men starting new exercise regimens have heart attacks, Kapalua's muddy ravines claim hikers, swimmers drown in Turtle Bay, and drivers distracted by Ka'anapali's rainbows drive off cliffs. I crept too close to Kilauea's flowing lava, seduced by its molten glow.

Tami Kagan-Abrams is a writer, wife, and mother in Los Angeles. Instagram *@kaganabrams*

Filing

He was sick of it. He left his filing clerk job in the bank and did another kind of bank job. Easy money, easy come, easy go; he was given ten years. He's still sick of filing, but is confident he'll get through the bars one of these days.

Nick Sweeney lives on the North Kent coast and, basically, makes stuff up. *nicksweeneywriting.com*

Visit

She stopped crying, tucked a gray-white strand of hair behind an ear, and took that day's note to him from her pocket. She pushed it down into the soft earth below her hip, felt the others there, and stood up. She kissed his headstone, then started back to her car.

William Cass has over 200 short stories published He is also the author of the short story collection, *Something Like Hope & Other Stories.*

Excavation

As she freed the ductwork segment from its fitting, it slipped from her hands. Amid the dust explosion, something skittered across the floor. She followed it with her eyes, then her feet. Despite a grimy coating, the object's turbinate shape revealed the long-dubious fate of her childhood pet hermit crab.

Elizabeth Barton is a writer/editor living in Chicago with her husband, two cats, and more than a little self-doubt. *lizardesque.wordpress.com*

Remember

Paul stands despite the force of fatigue pressing him down. The others keep vigil in the haze of the hospital overheads. "Remember the fun we had?" he says. "Remember the drives down River Road?"
"I re...mem..." she whispers.
Against the weight of morphine, his dying wife smiles.
Yes. She remembers.

Frank Diamond has numerous stories and poems published in various outlets.

Recompense

The retired man gazes at a treeless hillside across the sooty river. Deep gouges show where earth and rock were stripped for coal. Dark furrows lead to the black water. They carried the same ground on his hands and in his lungs. The price of his pension.

Gretchen Cowell is a retired paralegal and the author of *Help for the Child with Asperger's Syndrome*. ubcpress.ca/gretchen-mertz-cowell

His and Hers

The honeymooners photographed a dozen buddhas—buddhas golden, buddhas three-stories high, buddhas heaped in oranges and fresh flowers—before the guide explained no picture-taking in the temples. Immediately, the husband deleted his. Annoyed by his extravagant apology, the wife pretended to delete hers; the first of many secrets to come.

Meghan Wynne writes fiction and teaches English at a small liberal arts school in Ohio.

Spun Out

She inhabits a continually turning house. Dishes rattle. Jars roll under appliances. She wants to prune roses, but how? Is she facing the garden or the neighbor's cul-de-sac? HGTV's Property Brothers debate open floor plans. Sledge-hammers lift; she smashes her front door. The spinning stops. Dishes settle. Outside, rose petals.

Stephanie Barbe Hammer is a 6-time Pushcart prize nominee in fiction, poetry and nonfiction. *stephaniebarbehammer.net*

Reaganomics

During the meeting the CEO rabidly denounced big government as inefficient, touting that private businesses always use resources more effectively. Then he leaned back in his ivory-armed chair, took a nap, and made plans for his nine-week vacation. The lobbyists left to do what they were being (handsomely) paid for.

Ian Rogers lives in Toyama, Japan, where he also has a day job just like you. *butialsohaveadayjob.com*

Says Robbie

"Bird fly," says Robbie.
"Robbie, the bird is dead," I answer.
The bird jerks, then still.
"Bird deaded?" he asks. "What happens?"
"Dad comes home from work and takes the bird away in a plastic bag."
Silence. Robbie filtering thoughts through autism ... "What happens to the bag?"

Rachel Shapiro is a writer in Arizona and is currently working on *Says Robbie*.

The Perfect Crime

I planned it so carefully. Thought of every last detail. No fingerprints, no paper trail, no one ever knew what I had done. It was almost total perfection. Just one glaring oversight that I will never live down: I committed the crime on the night of my daughter's recital.

Jimmy Pappas is under the mistaken impression that his YouTube interview with Tim Green will provide him with a form of immortality.

A Pen

The manager handed her a pen. "Sell this to me." She was here to get a job selling bridal dresses—that she knew. Not pens. She tried and soon just repeated herself. On the way home, she thought of so much more to say. What she needed was a pen.

A special education teacher by day, Theresa Milstein writes middle grade, YA, and dabbles in poetry. *theresamilstein.blogspot.com*

Right of Way

On a narrow mountain path.
"I am walking North, you must back up."
"Nah, we are both going South; you turn back."
Five hours later.
"Whoever you are, I will not give way."
Most mountain ranges have passes.
But this range was renowned as the only one with an impasse.

Peter Snell was a bookseller and he wears a lot of red in December. Facebook *@Bartons.Bookshop*

Oops

A sunny afternoon, walking. He trips, loses his balance. Blood gushes from his head. Sound of flesh impacting rock far below. Sirens sound, emergency services arrive: her cliffside performance is worthy of an Oscar. Freedom from one type of mental torture beckons. She hasn't reckoned on another replacing it.

Karen Al-Ghabban is a lover of words and languages. Married, two children and a dog.

Working Girl

Found upright at the curb in the chill of dawn, the single blush-tinted stiletto was the last footprint she would leave on this earth, its mate too quick to step into the car of another faceless stranger. Tiny hands press against a window and wait for her return.

Pushcart nominee, Jayne Martin is also a recipient of Vestal Review's VERA award. Her debut flash collection, *Tender Cuts*, is published by Vine Leaves Press. *jaynemartin-writer.com*

Therapy Sessions

Sometimes I get overwhelmed listening all day to clients share their trauma—sexual assault, gun violence, physical abuse. Still, I tell them coming to me was a good first step. When I press my ink-filled needle into their flesh, they finally relax with the soothing pain of a new tattoo.

Kate Bradley-Ferrall is a Northern Virginia writer and artist, but not on bodies. Twitter *@KBFerrall*

Get the Hail Out

After a severe storm in April, an elderly woman found hail had covered the floor in her garage. While she began to panic, her neighbor, who was a landscaper, came by to see if she was ok. She smiled and politely asked him to get the hail out her garage.

Charles Gibson is a writer/editor who lives in Hendersonville, Tennessee and holds an Educational Specialist Degree.

Leopard Spots

"Grandpa, why are you growing spots?" asks little Georgie, fingering the back of my hand. The skin looks unfamiliar. 'That's not my hand,' I want to say, 'that's my grandfather's!' Instead, I tell him, "I'm turning into a leopard! Grrr!" Although to be honest, I feel anything but ferocious.

Chet Ensign wrote this in Wyoming where all the wildlife moved slow and stayed just out of sight.

The Settee

I was aware of the proprieties, I ignored the proprieties, captivated by her unexpected pallor, her callipygian dazzle covered in fine fabric. Her father, the CEO, wanted a male heir or so I'd convinced myself. I reached under her—"No," she said. We didn't get to stain her fine settee.

Clyde Liffey lives near the water. Twitter *@clydeliffey*

What's Important

Lara does what's important, and what's important is what Lara does. Believe me, she's a busy woman, which doesn't leave much time for my trivial concerns. The trick is to disguise the trivial as important. Tuesday nights are for making babies. In the dark, my vasectomy scar is undetectable.

Avery Mathers keeps bees and monitors moths in the Scottish Highlands, but mostly he writes. *averymathers.com*

Not How We Do It Here

The senior-most parent at the co-op preschool pursed her lips at how I yanked the stems off strawberries for our three-years-olds' snack. Abashed, I started slicing off the ends. She gasped. "May I?" With a paring knife, she carved a neat little circle around each stem. I'd been duly schooled.

Susmita Ramani lives in the San Francisco Bay Area, weaving worlds and embedding jewel-like people. Twitter @*susmitabythebay*

The Owlhoot Spring
(The Judge Said #1)

The James Gang stopped at my great-grandfather's farm. Their horses were thirsty. The Judge had a small spring back of the barn. All slaked. They weren't outlawish. The Judge said, "Not likely to find another spring in this dry season." Frank said, "We found yours. We'll find another." Jesse smiled.

Guinotte Wise welds steel sculpture and writes on a farm in Resume Speed, Kansas. *wisesculpture.com*

Water for Some

(The Judge Said #2)

The Judge said The James Gang stopped for water once. "What
did you do?"
"Gave 'em water."
"What would you do if Quantrill stopped by?"
"Give him a third eye middle of his forehead with that Kentucky
long rifle." He pointed over the fireplace with his pipe. He meant it.

Guinotte Wise welds steel sculpture and writes on a farm in Resume Speed,
Kansas. *wisesculpture.com*

Into the Darkness of Moby Dick

If you drive slowly and look for it, you just might find it, a faded
little seafood shack named for Melville's wicked white whale, the
parking lot covered in crushed shells that crunch nastily underfoot,
midday growing so dark with each step the crickets begin to chirp,
thinking it's night.

Howie Good's most recent poetry collection is *Gunmetal Sky*, available from Thirty
West Publishing.

Ocean

He goes to the ocean. He sits there for hours letting the sun touch his skin sore. The salt builds up in his sinus. Sneezes hurt. But he stays. Always looking out, searching for her ship, wave after wave, sun up sun down, the ocean stretching on forever, never ending.

Kate E Lore splits her time between a graphic and written memoir, screen plays, flash, comics, and her dating blog. *kateelore.com*

The Hunters

Young hunters mucking about the bog spied a monster. Black eyes fixed on them. Scaly feet were uprooted from the sediment as they pried the creature from its lair. "Wait until Mom sees this!" exclaimed the six-year-old as her brother loaded the huge snapper onto the Radio Flyer for transport.

A Jersey Girl at heart, Barbara Elliott lives, paints and writes in Philadelphia.

The Championships

Day Fight: Starring Blue Sky and White Cloud. Can Blue Sky defend their title? They look confident, but White Cloud rolls incredibly strong. Blue Sky is in trouble ... The Sun assists. **Winds howl:** "Evacuate! Lightning and Thunder ahead!" Blue Sky and White Cloud scarper over the Rainbow. Typical British weather.

Anneka Chambers is a Black British Poet and can also be found engaging in social activism. Instagram *@22poetrystreet*

This Is How The End Will Come

All summer, I swim. The ocean, my coldest, oldest friend, welcomes me. In drizzle, under coral-colored clouds or braving green-veined, wind-whipped rollers, I push ever deeper and speak aloud. "I love you water, love the pulse of your liquid life and each creature you extol and nurture. Bring me home."

Cordelia Frances Biddle's Martha Beale series is set in 1840's Philadelphia. *cordeliafrancesbiddle.net*

One Chance

The pedestrian crossing signal changed. Her eyes flicked to me once, my soul lurching into infinity. Everyone crossed but me. I should talk to her; I can't talk to her. My feet settled in concrete and seconds later she dwindled on the sidewalk. Over there, across the street. Then, gone.

Steve Ullom walks around central Illinois making notes about things that should be written down. *steveullom.com*

Compatibility

The receiver's lights flashed on. They were faint, but the beacon's signal was there. The unfathomable void of space and devastating eternity of time were not enough to stop it. It wasn't that it was powerful, it was just uniquely compatible. Finley tuned transponder and receiver to find each other.

B. Frederick Foley is a poet, writer, he spends his time living between Anchorage and Kasilof, Alaska.

A Stray Thought

I often thought it odd that, after the discovery of the mysterious Interstellar Conduits and nearly three centuries of space exploration, humanity had never come across another intelligent alien species. I mentioned it to Pam in the sauna.

"That is odd," she said, scratching the scales on her webbed fingers.

JJ Toner writes science fiction and enjoys music in his spare time. *JJToner.com*

Digital Death

His social media went dark. He didn't reply to emails or texts. Voicemail picked up his calls. The life he once lived, permanently displayed in images and comments posted in haste as he hiked, biked, climbed, and drove. His final photo snapped under the back end of a tractor-trailer.

Rita Riebel Mitchell lives in the Pinelands of South Jersey with her favorite beta reader. *RRMitchell.com*

Ginger Nut

Strolling about the sanctuary in duffle coats and fingerless gloves, the youngest, stashing ginger-nut biscuits in his pocket, asks about the friendliest donkey; 'His ribs!' I haven't prepared my children. I encourage the older ones to share treats. "Lucky we visited," I say, thinking some lives only have a past.

Maeve McKenna lives among words and trees, neither ever telling.

A Midlife Friday, 8:06pm

Ernest shuts his laptop. The den's sudden darkness feeling too heavy to wade across, he doesn't stand. Straight ahead, exactly where he wearily gazes, hangs a discolored photograph of himself—grinning, gowned and tossing a cap. But through the blackness, Ernest can't see himself.

Bea Boccalandro is the author of *Do Good At Work: How Simple Acts of Social Purpose Drive Success and Wellbeing*. *beaboccalandro.com*

Two Vowels

Two vowels went walking. The first did the talking. Complaining about the word they lived in. "It's too small. Plus, I don't even know what it means, do you?" The second vowel shook its head, quietly wondering where they were going. It was dark, getting darker, and almost bedtime.

Jason Heroux is currently the Poet Laureate for the City of Kingston, Ontario. *jasonheroux.blogspot.com*

Pop Quiz

Being abducted by aliens is like on TV, except for the pop quiz. I wasn't prepared to explain Justin Bieber to orange stalks of celery with blue leaves or to see them dance across the bridge of their ship, chirping in falsetto what sounded like "Oh baby baby oh baby."

Allene Nichols has recently moved to the beautiful state of Mississippi, where she continues to write, teach, and take photographs. *allenen.wordpress.com*

Bingo

There was a farmer who had a dog, and Bingo was his name-o. Or it might have been Ingo? Or Ngo? Or Go? Or O? Or a series of staccato handclaps? I don't know. That farmer kept changing his damn tune ...

Michael Walker is a writer living in Newark, Ohio. Facebook @*Indyauthor*

My Father's Desk

My father's working desk is a mess, despite retiring five years ago. I have to stop myself from rummaging around to see what he's been working on. But today, after he left for his morning stroll, I just couldn't resist. I found his to-do list. Item 1 read, "Happy."

Other than writing and translating, Stephanie Mamonto religiously lives her life as the Spanish proverb says: "The belly rules the mind." *stephaniemamonto. wixsite.com*

I'm Off

Skies above looming behind the smoke of clouds. Birds bleeping along the bones of trees. A chill loose in the morning air, fended off by bricks cooping up the world inside. I check my phone for the chance of rain, already assured of the certainty of peace and quiet.

Raymond Sloan lives and writes in County Down, Ireland.

Glances

I realize we are quite the sight but I could do without the double take, the surprised stare. Or worse the look of pity. When they see the Make-A-Wish button, they smile knowingly and take it as an invitation to talk. I just want to enjoy my vacation.

Lani Knutson writes about life as a mom to two boys with a rare disease in order to maintain her sanity. *oursepn1life.wordpress.com*

Karaoke

Your sister and her friends were so drunk and loud, we were all told to leave the Karaoke bar. Adamantly you insisted on doing one song before we left, and sang "What's New Pussy Cat" from the small and shabby stage. You were horrible, and I never loved you more.

Doug Mathewson writes very short fiction, and his book *Nomad Moon* is published by Cervena Barva Press.

The Follower

The dog sits at my gate every morning and night when I leave and come home from my office. I hate dogs which follow. Even after all this time she can still smell her owner's blood on my hands. Can you suggest me a way to get rid of it?

Prapti Gupta an 18-year-old girl from India who has been the author of the week in *StoryMirror*.

History of the World

Denise was a conscientious 5th grader. She took homework seriously. Made a perfect Styrofoam model of the solar system and painted each planet a toxic hue. Now, on a Caribbean beach flecked with tiny white balls she wonders, "Do they even try to teach truth in 5th grade these days?"

Deborah Nedelman is author of the novel *What We Take for Truth*, winner of the Sarton Women's Book Award for Historical Fiction. *DeborahNedelman.com*

The Ritual

She fixed her hair, applied some lipstick. Set a place for herself and for him. Filled his glass with wine, poured a little for herself. Waited. It'd been nearly 20 years since he'd walked out the door one sunny summer morning. Every day the same. Perhaps tonight he'd come home.

Cordelia Dietrich Zanger is a former award-winning TV news producer who now works as a fashion model. She loves a good story. Instagram *@cordelia.dietrich*

I Can't Stop Thinking

I can't stop thinking about someone I didn't really know. And now they are dead. I have six pictures of him on my phone. Some of them are live and if you hold it down with the volume on you can hear his laugh.

Ashton Russell lives and writes in Birmingham, Alabama.

Heart Stopper

The beast towered over the trees. Its roar shook the earth beneath their feet. Blood gushed through their bodies, pushing their hearts faster and faster. Until they stopped. All empty eyes and unfeeling limbs. Even as the beast bent down and sniffed, their screams never came.

Kailee Hayden is a graduation college student located in Pueblo, Colorado. Instagram @kay.xco

April Showers

After dad opened the door, we all shuffled into the house. A rumble echoed in the distance. A drop in air pressure pulled at our ears until it was upheaved by a gust of empty abandon. We accepted mom was gone. The rain didn't fall until the screams came out.

Emilee Prado's recent reads and artistic endeavours can be found on Instagram @_emilee_prado_

Transcendence

"My name is no longer David," I said to the alien. "We abandoned our earthly identities to ascend to the next level. As a result, we don't have names, things we love or hate, or even favorite colors." The creature scowled. "Well, there go my interview questions."

H. A. Eugene lives in Brooklyn, where he writes strange stories and constructs elaborate theories about the true intentions of cats. *haeugene.tv*

Dark Crescents: A Mini-Saga

There they remain, perpetually dark and crescent-like. Swooping down and across, a blend of indigo and charcoal. They lack appeal and reflect the enervation within. Just like that, the dark crescents vanish from sight. The beauty blender worked its magic as the concealer spread under and around the eyes.

Alyssa Walzak is a budding writer and blogger on the East Coast. *wingingitwithwalzak.com*

The Boughs of Yesteryear

After an outdoor play, we trekked east in the Central Park dark to a restaurant where my girlfriend snapshot her meal. I asked the waitress how to navigate something on my plate. She forked a morsel in my mouth with her fingers, making me wish I'd kept my mouth shut.

Frank De Canio loves music from Bach to Amy Winehouse and attends a Café Philo in Lower Manhattan.

Why?

"I hate this coffee."
"Why?"
"Because the smell makes me sick."
"Why?
"Because it reminds me of me."
"Why?"
"Because I haven't showered in six months."
"Why?"
"Because I don't want to taste nice."
"Why?"
"Because there's something in my plughole. Something that scares me."

Andrew Jackson is a student and writer from Surrey, UK, who is working on his first sci-fi novel. *andrewsfiction.com*

It Was Dusk

It was dusk. She crossed over the bridge to the Lyn. The sea was all around. Her husband walked behind her. A love letter from his pocket jumped at her this morning, causing hurt. She wished he was dead. She looked back, and he was gone, leaving no trace.

Kanta Walker is a painter and a poet she spends much time reading YA science fiction.

It's not Fibromyalgia

I have that sharp stabbing pain again. A breeze. And something brushes gently past. Instinctively I turn. Nothing there. I can see perfectly—I'm not blind—but I know they're there. In my space. Experimenting on me. Again.

Christine Ries is an avid reader, enjoys wordsmithing with author friends, and is fascinated by tiny stories.

Always

"Who thought you'd be just mine always?" Gretchen smiled, face in her husband's shoulder. Greg patted her brown hair gone gray. With his free hand, he reread his phone: Tomorrow! Yay! texted from the lovely Sylvia who liked to do more than cuddle. And who made staying married still possible.

Shoshauna Shy loves the endless possibilities inherent in flash fiction, and how it triggers poetry, and vice versa.

The Mirror

Mr. Galway said, "Would you love me the way I look at myself in the mirror?" The Mirror shined once and then Galway's reflection was gone. "Hello? Hello? Are you there? Hello?"

George Zamalea is a writer who lives in Lancaster, California

The Laugh

He puts on his black jacket. Where are you going? she says.
Doesn't matter. I won't be back.
Why not?
You're the human version of an autistic dog. You don't mind having me around but you don't really care either way.
The door closed. She starts laughing and can't stop.

Bob Shea has a checkered past which includes juggling, fire-eating, writing in New York and elsewhere.

Willow

Our ancient willow's 50-foot-long limb snapped, crashed to the wet spring grass. Rain, wind, or the simple weight of years. The two oriole nests of summers past still droop from the ribbon leaves left. Come back, come back. "Ancient?" but they live to seventy at most. Let go, let go.

Sarah Van Arsdale is a writer, artist and teacher living in the Catskills of New York State. *sarahvanarsdale.com*

My Friend

I learned about my friend's death on Facebook. She refused to see me when I flew out to Santa Fe; I didn't know why. We met in kindergarten. I liked her red plaid dress and braids. I should have barged in and demanded to see her. Now it's too late.

Robin Stein lives and writes in Massachusetts. She teaches writing workshops and likes piano, dancing and people-watching. *robinsteincreative.com*

Acoustics

I wanted to be a drummer, but my mother, who'd never heard of "Moe" Tucker, said, "Girls don't drum." My daughter-in-law teaches music, and for six years she's been giving drum lessons in my basement. I'd forgiven Mother long ago, but it took 40 years for me to understand her.

Miriam Kotzin, author of *Debris Field* and *Country Music*, teaches literature and creative writing.

Returns

They always managed to pull her from the register when he arrived. The old man was missing an ear like Van Gogh. He reeked of filth and beer, his bottles and cans unwashed. She touched each one like it held the plague and handed him the coins. She exhaled.

A special education teacher by day, Theresa Milstein writes middle grade, YA, and dabbles in poetry. *theresamilstein.blogspot.com*

Parting Shot

The solicitor handed me a letter from my mother, whom we had just buried. I opened it, expecting words of comfort. "There was never a right time," she'd written, "to tell you that you were conceived as a result of a violent rape. He died in jail. I always loved you."

Karen Al-Ghabban is a lover of words and languages. Married, two children and a dog.

Vintage

Rick warned me, "Department brunches are initiation rites." Behold—astride limp lettuce, glistening tomato aspic! McDade's in his kitchen again. The TV tray wobbles when Rick pokes his unyielding aspic; it tumbles onto the sky-blue velvet sofa, bounces to the floor. He dispatches the evidence lickety-split, then mutters, "Firewalking's next."

Miriam Kotzin, author of *Debris Field* and *Country Music*, teaches literature and creative writing.

Thanksgiving

More vegetables, dear? You don't really need another biscuit. Easy on the gravy, darling. Pie anyone? No whip cream, honey. I nibble at my allotted portions that are nowhere near sufficient. It's true. I am large, yet Mother is peerless at reducing me to nothing at all.

Pushcart nominee, Jayne Martin is also a recipient of Vestal Review's VERA award. Her debut flash collection, *Tender Cuts*, is published by Vine Leaves Press. *jaynemartin-writer.com*

Relative

She recalled her days of food stamps and WIC, pregnant, homeless, no car. Not even McDonald's would hire her with her obvious abdomen. The memory felt petty now as she watched thirteen slate-faced girls on TV marched through the dusty village, machine guns pressed against their backs.

Katherine Gotthardt is an award-winning poet and author who, until now, dreamed of going to India. *KatherineGotthardt.com*

Honey Cake

"Samson's riddle may have been unfair," he said, "but Delilah was a treacherous bitch."
"Enjoying your honey cake?" I asked.
"You've made better. Too sweet."
"And you're sweet enough." I smiled.
The honey cake was sweet enough too. Just sweet enough to hide the poison, bitter as my shriveled heart.

Nettie Thomson is a Scottish writer who is growing her hair. *nettiethomson.com*

Paper Cut

At a Manhattan cafe.
Patron: "An espresso to go please."
Barista: "I don't serve 'espresso to go.' The shot is very sensitive, and it doesn't interact well with the paper."
Patron: "???####!!!"
Barista: "Oh, okay. I'll put it in a demitasse cup and *you* can pour it in the paper."

Jan Bartelli is a former journalist, a more-or-less retired attorney and a less-is-more writer of creative non-fiction.

Talcum Powder

"That's us in like a hundred years," Leslie said, her shoulder grazing his as she pointed to the tin-type of his great grand-parents, wrinkled as dry apples but still beaming. The scent of talcum powder scrambled his head. A century? He couldn't picture the next five minutes.

Chet Ensign writes in northern New Jersey, inventing things that live beyond the outdoor lights.

Long Island Iced Tea

Are you cheating? My question hangs between us, fermenting in the citrus-perfumed atmosphere.
I'm not. Bitterness seeps from his words as he slices sunshine yellow lemons.
I don't believe you.
He wipes his stained hands.
I saw you. I say to his back, caressing the chef's knife.
The teakettle hisses.

Jass Aujla plans perfect (fictional) murders during her boring day-job meetings. *jassaujla.com*

Once or Twice

"Have you ever spoken to someone and felt something tugging at your insides, like an invisible cricket sounding imminent death alarms, screaming *THIS IS THE LAST TIME!*," Kaitlin asked her sister, both expecting and hoping that she wasn't alone. The truth is it had happened to her before—twice.

Katherine Shehadeh is an attorney and student, who enjoys small writing and her small kids. *katherinesarts.com*

How I Know I'm Not Crazy

The powdered milk momentarily floats on the black coffee. A spoonful of brown sugar scatters the powder, a few crystals clinging to the edges of white remnants. I imagine they are Viking huts on snow-covered islands off Greenland in the 980s. This is how I know I'm not crazy.

Richard LeBlond is a retired biologist and active writer and photographer still alive in North Carolina.

South of the Border

Trading shots with him, I chased Pancho Villa on horseback last night through burning dreams of the Chihuahuan Desert, and when I woke up dry-mouthed and sweaty and feeling as though I had never slept, the rain falling in the street sounded like the clicking claws of Mexican scorpions.

Howie Good's most recent poetry collection is *Gunmetal Sky*, available from Thirty West Publishing.

Rain Remembered

The rain was cold that day. I shivered under it. But we were already there so why not? I jumped in a puddle to splash you. You kicked out to get me back. We laughed. Now whenever it rains, I think of you. Always looking in puddles expecting your reflection.

Kate E Lore splits her time between a graphic and written memoir, screen plays, flash, comics, and her dating blog. *kateelore.com*

Hospital Bed

Shoes squeak as my bed is rolled under bright lights. I'm asked to count backwards from 100. I no longer feel the pain. I see no blood. Tears slide down my temples and into my ears. I strain to hear "Twin. Girls". But I hear no cries.

Diane Minerath, aspiring writer, lives in Coeur d'Alene ID, with her husband and two dogs.

It's All About Cash on the Table

My family, they were leeches. I left 'em all I had, 700 cash on the kitchen table, then split.
Worked my way down the coast. HELP WANTED, it could mean anything. I was jazzed every time I opened a door. Got me a bunch of nowhere jobs. You want cream with that?

Miriam Kotzin, author of *Debris Field* and *Country Music*, teaches literature and creative writing.

T-Minus

The rockets roar. Tears fill my eyes. Am I happy or terrified to achieve this lifelong goal? We ascend, slowly at first, and then faster than humans should move. A thin metal shell made by Man protects us as we kiss the cold and dark of instant death, space tourists.

Vic Larson writes poetry, essays, fiction and movie reviews. He lives in Florida with his wife Jeanne.

You Never Come; You Go.

I watch you walk out the back door, or the door to the basement, or the door to the bathroom. The house is a sideways maze of doors and shirt tails and weakening hands trailing around corners. You never come; you go. And then I remember: you passed last night.

Keith Hoerner (BS, MFA) lives, teaches, and pushes words around in Southern Illinois

Dark Again

Dark again, back inside, they switch on a light, and then another, before switching them both off again, and then turning on two different lights in another part of the house, before switching them off too, until they are alone in the darkness once more where they can see themselves just fine.

J Kane for the moment lives beside a flat mountain top in Australia, currently reading Francis Picabia. Instagram *@via.launmobb*

Trending

After Thursday's meeting, the official Community Spies assumed their duties, peeking through windows and listening at keyholes, the latest tools for digital snooping fully deployed, the volunteer Town Scolds parsing infractions and deviations in every thought as they prowled the streets shouting, "You're wrong! You're wrong!" at everyone who passed.

Chuck Augello is the author of *The Revolving Heart*, a Best Books of 2020 selection by Kirkus Reviews. *thedailyvonnegut.com*

Night Running

Moon fat, and so many stars. Shadows of cacti and mesquite trees. You stumble, catch yourself. You imagine tripping over the canyon's edge, your bones bleaching lighter each year, like the animal bones you pass in the daylight, so beautiful, so calm. Sometimes, you almost wish for this to happen.

In idle moments, Cinthia Ritchie wonders if she's a writer with a running obsession or a runner with a writing obsession. *cinthiaritchie.com*

If Only

If only they had woken me to say they were leaving. I traipsed up and down the house, sure that I had made them disappear. I packed my backpack with gummy bears, and set off to save the world, only to find them at the corner, getting me ice cream.

rani Jayakumar loves coming up with ideas and making lists. *okachiko.com*

The Deer Head

He looked down at me. His dark eyes seeming to watch my every move. "I didn't do it," I screamed. But I had. And now the lamp I'd knocked over was leaking kerosene across the floor and gentle flames were lapping at the wall below his all-knowing stare.

Lori Narlock is a Napa-based reader, writer, and cook. Instagram *@lorinarlock*

Fascist

The morning brightened. Grandma sat on the sofa after her breakfast. Her nine-year-old grandson came to her and asked, "Grandma, what is fascist?" Grandma was shocked. "Where from you get this word?" she said. "From brother, he said Dad behaving like a fascist."

Shaheer Pulikkal is a young Indian short story writer and poet.

The Guitarist

He dedicated his life to music, but his only regular gigs were teaching guitar. He managed to save enough to buy a new Volkswagen Beetle without heat to save money. When times got really tough, he slept in it. There was always a thick blanket in the trunk.

A special education teacher by day, Theresa Milstein writes middle grade, YA, and dabbles in poetry. *theresamilstein.blogspot.com*

The Contract

He wrote it on a cocktail napkin. He said it was still binding, even if he'd written it on banana peel, as long as we both signed it. The bartender was a witness. I promised him complete fidelity while he was deployed. He promised me he'd return. We both lied.

Pushcart nominee, Jayne Martin is also a recipient of Vestal Review's VERA award. Her debut flash collection, *Tender Cuts*, is published by Vine Leaves Press. *jaynemartin-writer.com*

Damned Flies

If not for the flies, I'd have missed them. Hungry, alert to every sound, they crouched in brown underbrush. Only their swatting tails gave them away. I froze, relieved when they turned to move on. But the damn flies; ow! When I looked up, I saw they'd seen me, too.

Chet Ensign wrote this in Wyoming where all the wildlife moved slow and stayed just out of sight.

After Her Husband Passed

Jeannie worked all winter as a cook in the Alberta oil camp. While standing next to the window in her Newfoundland kitchen, she said, "I have always loved this view of the harbor," and I could hear in her voice the dread of winters to come.

Richard LeBlond is a retired biologist and active writer and photographer still alive in North Carolina.

Revenge

Furious, she stopped speaking to her husband. She painted her face a flat white and drew on black brows and a red mouth; She pressed her gloved palms flat against invisible glass, her silent prison. Because she was silent, he was content. He continually hummed her favorite song, always off-key.

Miriam Kotzin, author of *Debris Field* and *Country Music*, teaches literature and creative writing.

Washing Up

My neighbor stands in her kitchen, framed. I avoid looking through her window, listen instead to cutlery and crockery. A single wineglass is silent; tonight: a clink, the dog: unsettled. I sneak a peek as a man's broad torso retreats down the next-door hallway, towel slung around his waist.

Nicole Melanson is a writer, poet, and essayist who also edits WordMothers, supporting women's work in the literary arts. *nicolemelanson.com*

Cervical 4

She saw the boy dive as the wave receded: body slicing through air; sand like concrete. He rode the next wave facedown, limbs floating like driftwood. She splashed to his rescue, dragged his deadweight body to shore. Saved his life, they said. He spent the rest of it hating her.

Kathleen Latham plays with words and spoils her cat. *KathleenLatham.com*

Keeping

I did not lie, but kept the secrets, the moments that accumulated as the world dissembled. That's how I explained it to myself. Contriving the next distraction, in an attempt to avoid discovery, became routine. Mastering the art of outer calm. I was shocked, at the same time, energised.

Jenny Dunbar is a busy writer and potter, based in the UK.

Last Time Around

Neon light burned on the ruined trees across the road from the motel. He didn't know the woman much, but she said she liked the way he played at authority. Gazing out from the passenger window, she pushed her red hair out of her face and muttered, *I'd rather die.*

Steven Ostrowski is a widely published writer and painter. Twitter *@sostrow2*

The Newlyweds

She approaches at the reception—in the presence of his bride!—to say he'd been her first mad love. Stunned, he admits she'd been his first mad love. So what to make of it now? His wife smiles and excuses herself. Remember The Graduate? she says. Let's catch the bus.

Learn about Claude Clayton Smith at his website: *claudeclaytonsmith.wordpress.com.*

A Carer's Life

He closed the shop for the last time and sighed. Retirement was going to be wonderful. His travel plans were set and he would soon be visiting his brother in Australia. That night his mother had a stroke. Two years later he was still there ...

Peter Snell was a bookseller and he wears a lot of red in December. Facebook *@Bartons.Bookshop*

Supermarket Cowboy

Obedient carts return to their corral, but others balk, need to be herded back from the far edges of the asphalt lot, wheels squeaking protest. After closing I set them in a circle. I take my guitar out of my trunk and serenade them under the moon.

Marjorie Tesser is a writer, editor, and teacher who always returns her shopping cart. Facebook *@marjorietesserwriter*

Untethered

"Don't let me linger," Momma had told me. Now, her tether to this world is no longer a cord engorged with life, like the one that brought her into it. When I tell the doctor it's time, I feel Momma's lips brush my cheek as I set her free.

Traci Mullins is a non-fiction book editor by day, thus, reading and writing fiction is her play.

Sunday morning for Simon the atheist

He wakes humming a melody he can't place. Tenderly, he picks butter lettuce from the garden, and gathers eggs from the chickens, thanking them by name. He thinks of the day ahead. Bill would need a hand. The usual paper shoots under his doorway. Repent! Simon will forgive its author.

Aisha Wiley lives in eastern Pennsylvania and dabbles in flash, poetry, and the lyric essay.

The Unknown

Facing away from the door, she slips her hand into the purse at her waist. It's quiet, but tension sparks the air around her. The cool steel gun barrel in her grasp gives her confidence. And she waits. This could turn out bad or very, very bad.

Antonia Albany is an author and blogger and lives in the wine country of Northern California with her tripod kitty. *thejoyofaginggratefully.com*

Better to Not Give

The disheveled man sitting on NYC's Lexington and Third avenues holds a cardboard sign that reads *Homeless and Hungry*.
I avert my eyes and walk by. His calls out after me: "No good deed goes unpunished."
I pause, and turn. "Am I good, then?"
He gives me a thumbs up.

Jan Bartelli is a former journalist, a more-or-less retired attorney, and a less-is-more writer of creative non-fiction.

The Barista

The guy ahead of me plastered the barista with explicit instructions for his caffeinated concoction, a hot brewed latte with salted cream foam, low fat milk and whipped whale sperm. Finally he left.
"An Americano, black," I said.
"That's it?" The Barista asked. I nodded.
"Thank you!" She smiled.

Howard Dart Humeston earned a Masters of Science degree in nonsense while working in higher education. He resides in a small town in south central Florida.

Postponed

I once swore I would start smoking again when I'm eighty-five years old, then I pushed it to ninety. What I didn't know was that life would become more precious as I aged. Can I really postpone all addictions to the presumed end of my life? This might not work.

Catherine Klatzker's newest book is *You Will Never Be Normal* from Stillhouse Press. *catherine.klatzker.com*

Soul Music

"Your soul yearns for light. Make way for the sun's million rays to find it. And dance within." His mother woke him with this song every childhood morning. When life closed in on her, he sang her song. To her. For her soul to wake to light in her afterlife.

Read about Chitra Gopalakrishnan at *chitragopalakrishnan.com.*

Water Words

My words trickle onto waiting leaves. Teardrop syllables hang from the wind-blown green tips. The soil below becomes their refuge, receiving tragic sentences from gray clouds. Memories that live inside the rain can sometimes become uncomfortable. The sky thunders, then darkens. Things unexpected painfully grow from falling words.

Pittershawn Palmer is a writer who enjoys dancing with words. *pittershawn.com*

Service Industry

The drummer's band played at all the local bars and was well known. What sucked was all the dental work he needed with no insurance. So he went to the local university and let the students use him for practice. The bastards still charged him for his services.

A special education teacher by day, Theresa Milstein writes middle grade, YA, and dabbles in poetry. *theresamilstein.blogspot.com*

Thigh Food

There were fisheries patrol officers on the wharf, so she slipped her two illegal salmon into each leg of her pants, which were tucked into her boots. Walking right past the patrol officers, she drove off in her truck, the salmon still nestled with her legs.

Richard LeBlond is a retired biologist and active writer and photographer still alive in North Carolina.

Love

Many things go unspoken; the Kids, Bills, my Breast Cancer, and his Alcoholism. I see our love reflected in his eyes. Sometimes they're so dark I can't see his pupils. I lie to myself, *something is still there*, even though I can't see it.

Emily Kupinsky is a Creative Artist, Writer & Maker of things. Instagram *@emmysez*

Love's Perspectives

He calls me "Baby" and "Little Darling." All night, I sleep by his side, curling my body into his. When I'm cold he covers me with a blanket. I would kill for this person. Why is it, then, that he admonishes me for chasing squirrels? Dead, each would prove my devotion.

Cordelia Frances Biddle's Martha Beale series is set in 1840's Philadelphia. *cordeliafrancesbiddle.net*

Silence

We met as seatmates in the last row of a Greyhound bus. He was deaf, so we exchanged notes. "I had to be somewhere else," he wrote, and I understood. Later, in the dark, we held hands and dozed, partners in travel, seeking comfort as we headed into the unknown.

Now living in San Francisco, Laura is an editor who writes for pleasure and pain. *jacobylm.net*

The Cactus and the Lemon

"Why so happy?" asked the cactus. The lemon tree contemplated this question as fruits were plucked from its branches by birds and coyotes. "Because the creatures love me, can't you see?" The cactus poked itself into a lemon, freeing its sour nectar. It then shrugged and whispered, "Is that so?"

K.R. Schraeder is a writer, poet, and cat enthusiast living in San Diego, California. *kaschraeder.wixsite.com*

Out of Mind

Outside her bedroom window, the branch of the old oak tree reaches out. In the light of the moon it's ragged and twisted, like the hand of a witch. She switches on her lamp to make it disappear, but knows it's still there, hiding behind her reflection in the glass.

Sarah Beth Martin writes novels, short stories, and other slices of life from her home in coastal Maine. *sarahbethmartin.com*

Götterdämmerung

I glance at the sign outside the church when I should be watching the road. *Love Like Jesus*, it says. Nice sentiment, I think, as the sun sets in a profusion of toxic colors, like the chemical tanker burning intently at the edge of the world.

Howie Good's most recent poetry collection is *Gunmetal Sky*, available from Thirty West Publishing.

Senior Trip

Drunk and wallowing in self-pity, she stood at the edge, hoping to end it all. No one would laugh at her again. As a cheering crowd gathered below, she jumped from the balcony. A school chaperone helped her out of the pool, gave her a towel, and called her parents.

A former teacher, Rita Riebel Mitchell writes both at home and on road trips. She lives in New Jersey. *RRMitchell.com*

Quenched

Scientists claim that water is alien. An intergalactic hitchhiker, secreted in ice, carried on asteroids. Even so, our bodies crave it. I think of this as you breathe beside me. Wonder what I would have become if you never arrived. I would thirst for you, I think. I would want.

Kathleen Latham plays with words and spoils her cat. *KathleenLatham.com*

Mafia Romance Crap

"We had an arranged marriage, your mother and I. Much later we fell in love."
"Straight outta some mafia romance crap," he muttered, disinterested.
If only he'd met my conservative father and counted the bride money.

Neelima is a student of literature from India, in love with words and all things bookish.

Guided Tour

Tessa always loved animals. When she was young, she started getting them tattooed. First, a butterfly on one shoulder. Then an iguana on her arm and a dragon on her back. Now, in her old age, Tessa has a dermatological zoo. To go through it, you must ask her permission.

Marcelo Medone is a writer from Buenos Aires, Argentina. He loves microfiction. Instagram @marcelomedone

Chili

This morning the chili plant on the windowsill greeted her with two perfectly formed minuscule peppers. Hesitating over her choice, she picked the left, leaving the other looking forlorn. Nobody was to take the other pepper today, since she was due to die.

Nelly Shulman is an author of five popular historical novels in Russian. *nellyshulman.com*

White Vans

Blank, white vans from unknown places, go to unknown destinations, with unidentified goods, and shadowy drivers. They park in odd places as if abandoned, or else are backed into storehouses so their contents are never seen. I need a god to explain white vans.

Garry McDougall is an Australian author who lets the world speak for itself, or else indulges in coffee.

Scarecrow

As the sun set, the farmer looked at all the crows in his field despite the Scarecrow. "You can't even scare one crow," said the farmer. "Crows?" the Scarecrow said through needle-sharp teeth as it climbed down from its post. "I'm not here to scare crows."

Ralph Gibson is a museum professional in Northern California who has been writing stories since he was five years old.

Measuring Up

"Mr. Evans?" The dark suited man smiled broadly on the doorstep. "Your wife forgot to leave your measurements, thought I'd drop round personally."
Tom frowned, puzzled.
"I must congratulate you, sensible to think ahead—but, have you considered the Regal Oak? Our premium model? Silk lined with brass handles."

Rosie Cullen is a novelist and short story writer living in Manchester UK; *The Lucky Country* was published in April 2021. *rmcullenauthor.wordpress.com*

Water Wings

Jake has the lake, house, balloons, helium, birthday cake and floatie, but no bike pump. He blows into the deflated floatie until he's light-headed—the limp flamingo, another lurid reproach. He decides the floatie's a fancy balloon. Tethered to the dock all day, the helium-filled flamingo hovers over its reflection.

Miriam Kotzin, author of *Debris Field* and *Country Music*, teaches literature and creative writing.

Life and Death

Burying birds like they matter grounds life—interrupted. Considering his future, the sand methodically passes from shovel to hole and back until a single feather remains in view. Trying to escape fate, our feather overcomes the grave, drawn by the ocean's current. Rest in power.

Lisa Carlson is a wife, mother, teacher, writer and concerned human seeking refuge in the written word.

The Midnight Sun

The midnight sun in Fairbanks, Alaska, paints the western sky red
and orange. The eastern sky echoes its warm glow. On this summer
solstice, the day never seems to end. Even the birds chirp their merry
tune before dawn arrives as I run alone, a virtual midnight sun run.

Kwan Kew Lai is an author, a Harvard medical faculty physician, an infec-
tious disease specialist, a disaster response volunteer, an artist, and a runner.
kwankewlai.com

A Hospital Drama

The high-pitched whistle was followed by a barely audible crump;
then all hell was let loose. None of the Palestinian staff or patients
could be found; the windows and light bulbs were all shattered. As
the dust settled, and all was quiet, nobody heard the next wave of
attack aircraft.

Peter Snell was a bookseller and he wears a lot of red in December. Facebook
@Bartons.Bookshop

Sweet

Eating a ripe peach in the summer sunshine in my middle-life years, I realize that this is what it's all about. I had a long spring: decades of stretching roots and limbs into unlikely places, drawing a wealth of learning from discomfort and discovery. Now, it's time to make something sweet.

Sarah Griffin lives in Syracuse, New York, and is a writer and the managing editor of the occasional online publication, *The Elephant. theelephant.press*

Black Hole

I marveled at the tiny hieroglyphics glittering in the twilight, and wondered if I sat on the lip of a black hole, where time does not exist, where history slows, and where all ether is devoured, would I be absent mortality, tethered to eternity?

Paul Rousseau is a semi-retired physician and writer languishing in the sauna called South Carolina.

And Then She Danced

The phonograph was wound and the record placed. The stylus came down and then she danced. She remembered the scent of a thousand roses. "She's doing it again, isn't she?" he asked, waking slightly and punching his pillow. "Yes," he answered. "She's dancing again. I can smell the roses."

Michael Yoder is a writer living in Victoria, B.C. Canada

Missing

Summer began with her departure. Keys left in the ignition. White cloth caught on a fence nail. Cast-off pattern. Each day, dogs pulled leashes toward acres of Montana wheatgrass. Nothing. The constellation of flashlights gave up once fields were mowed too close to hide a body. Redshift. Grief: Polaris, ever.

Jacqueline Ahl's absurdist one-acts have been produced in NY, MO, and NC, receiving national and international awards. Facebook @jacqueline.ahl

She Loved the Nights

She loved the nights. The days cooled off to a perfect twenty-five celsius and fluorescent bulbs replaced the sun. Holes in the walls opened into neon caverns guarded by high-heeled entrepreneurs. Loud music drowned out the despair of life and its loneliness. Here, delusion was everything.

Lindsay Erdman is a Visual Arts educator, artist, writer and musician based in Toronto, Canada. *lindsayerdman.net*

Easing Restrictions

"What are you doing?"
I look up at her reflection in the bathroom mirror, watching me with arms folded. I tip my head back to prevent the white foam spilling out before replying.
"I'm brushing my teeth."
She nods, as if she had expected this all along.
"Who is she?"

Daniel Gooding is a writer of other very short stories featured in 101 Fiction, 101 Words, Dog-Ear and Drabblez. Twitter *@dp_gooding*

You're Poison Ivy

I chase the maddening itch across the dotted landscape of winter-pale skin. The red flush signaling the intolerable sensation spreading daily, forearm to forearm, hip to swollen lip. Pills and pungent poultices soothe the explosion of histamine activating my immune system against the treachery of those caustic oils.

Nina Miller wants you to protect yourself against back yard dangers like poison ivy and ticks.

Surprise

Creeping up the back stairs by moonlight, leaving discarded clothes in her wake, she anticipated his delight she'd returned early. Aroused and naked, she quietly opened the bedroom door, planning to slip between the sheets, next to him. She retreated, deflated, broken: there was no space.

Karen Al-Ghabban is a lover of words and languages. Married, two children and a dog.

Saturday Morning on the Bike Trail

Because he rode a recumbent bike, the fall wasn't much to comment on. But the way he didn't move—well. Other bikers called 911, someone started chest compressions. Two women pulled up close, folded their hands in prayer. Only his wife, now whistling, continued on her way down the trail.

Joanne Nelson enjoys biking on Saturday mornings. She is the author of *This Is How We Leave*. More information can be found at *wakeupthewriterwithin.com*

What Not to Keep

Frank damned his cracking chubby ankles. At the door, he discovered Lizbeth—and their infant. She handed off the sack, poured two bourbons. Watching *The Keepers*, Frank figured the nun did it. Floorboards creaked. Metal slashed through his arm. It was his wife, the one who washed the whiskey glasses.

Read about Annette J. Wick at her website: *annettejwick.com*

Theodore

Theodore never said no. He'd cover your shift, lend you a Ben Franklin, whatever. Even in his watery grave, his poltergeist satiates those who summon his spirit. Yes, the ouija board always reads. Everyone loves him. I do fear, however, that his regard would wane if the planchette did too.

John Sexton is a highschool student from South Florida who is interested in studying English in college. Instagram *@john.sextonn*

The Bud

I am a bud about to bloom, gorgeous and gregarious.
"To prune is to bloom" are the only words spoken.
Nipped in the bud.
Detached, descending.
Bud falls faster than flower.
Voiceless. Crushed. Stomped into the earth.
I spring up. I speak up. A new day has risen.

Paul Hertig teaches Global Studies courses and has dabbled with creative writing ever since majoring in English Literature at the University of Minnesota.

Wisdom

My ex-husband had all the answers. He was always saying things like, "If you don't want ants to spoil your picnic, you should leave the food at home." If I'd taken his advice, I could've saved myself a lot of trouble. I would've had a long life—but no picnics.

Miriam Kotzin, author of *Debris Field* and *Country Music*, teaches literature and creative writing.

After All

Her boyfriend called her at work, crying and incoherent. She tried to understand, but the fragments—car—police—only made it worse.
She sped the thirty minutes in twenty.
He was out, and his room reeked of vomit.
She realized she was dating someone like her father after all.

A special education teacher by day, Theresa Milstein writes middle grade, YA, and dabbles in poetry. *theresamilstein.blogspot.com*

Dog Alarm

The dog is set for 7:30. It drinks before it goes off, so it will be wet. There will be some growling and several barks. Refuse to respond, and it will pull off the covers and pile them by the door. There is no way to turn it off.

K. T. Maclay is an occasional writer and teacher living in Oaxaca de Juarez, Mexico

Judith

Judith painted pears with personality, among many other things. Five lively pears, clearly in conversation, adorn my wall. The one in the middle is reclining, relaxing and laughing, bent as if holding its belly. The two off to the side are whispering secrets. These pears live on, Judith, as do you.

Connie Biewald writes and teaches—and works hard to be kind, which doesn't always come naturally. *conniebiewald.com*

Peanut Butter

Offering four-year-old Elvis a peanut butter and jelly sandwich on a plate, "Mister, I hate peanut butter on top."
"Try closing your eyes, Elvis." I quickly flip the sandwich over. "Okay, open."
Elvis shrieks, "How'd you do that!"
Later, he asks, "Mister, can you turn this penny into a quarter?"

Mark Hurtubise, after a four-decade hiatus, is creating again from the Pacific Northwest by balancing on a twig like a pregnant bird.

Benched

Woody, on a park bench overlooking the empty sun-bleached August baseball diamond, feels his eighty years. Heat be damned, once he'd have been down there swinging. The barefoot girl in short-shorts, hips rolling, crosses the diamond, gladdening his eye without mitigating the feeling of having been benched.

James Gallant was the the winner of 2019 Schaffner Press Prize for music-in-literature for his story collection, La Leona, and Other Guitar Stories.

In the Scheme of Things

Clambering up the spiral staircase to the roof, a chain of suited, chortling corporates, carrying card viewers, glasses, and Bolly. Outside, the August sun dims, as dusk arrives at lunchtime. Birds roost. Those brash city dwellers watch the solar eclipse in silent contemplation, knowing that words would ruin the moment.

Karen Al-Ghabban is a lover of words and languages. Married, two children and a dog.

Grass

Three fat men came up the stairs. I got a bat wrapped around my head. Taekwondo kicked in and it saved my life. I didn't bubble up, so the police ruined me. To be a grass, or to not be a grass. Three fat men came up the stairs ...

Rob Reid is currently working on an automated Betting BOT and his own language called SCRAPE. *skrewballed.blogspot.com*

Murakami

Clair finished the Murakami book, placed it on the bar, then downed her beer. She lit a cigarette, reflecting on what she had just read. Deep in thought, she caught the gaze of a man two stools down. They made mad love with their eyes and then she vanished.

Shane Huey writes prose and the occasional haiku from his home in sunny South Florida. *shanehuey.net*

For the Love of Ice Cream

My daughter and I smother our sundaes in sprinkles and syrup. Grandma took hers plain.
She said, "I love you," plain too. "No need to ornament something so sweet."
Today, I took my sundae plain, and said to my daughter, "I love you." We never asked for toppings again.

Raquel Battaglia is a social psychology researcher who uses writing to explore the qualitative nature of the human experience. Instagram *@raquel_fancy.rachel*

My New Book

My new book, *How I Succeeded In Life With Humility* is now available for forty-six dollars at most upscale bookstores and websites around the world.

Fred Miller is a California writer. *pookah1943.wordpress.com*

Little Red

"What big eyes you have! Oh! What big teeth you have," she squealed. Then, "Gimme a break," in her real voice. Eye roll. Did it actually think she couldn't tell the difference? The fur was a dead giveaway. She strode home, basket swinging, beast's head inside.

Erin Dionne writes novels and picture books for kids, flash fiction for adults, and lives outside of Boston with her husband, two children, and a disgruntled dog. *erindionne.com*

The Play

Time was running out. Bumped from centerfield by a thirteen-year-old who ran everything down, I had to make a play. The ball arced to center right. We sprinted under it. He called me off. I rammed into his space. I felt triumphant until the ball clunked off my glove.

Gretchen Cowell is a retired paralegal and the author of *Help for the Child with Asperger's Syndrome.*

Theo

The first time Gunter glimpsed Theo, an uncontrollable fear crashed over him. Theo, a boy blessed by the gods: Apollo's looks; Athena's poise; and the power of Atlas. One glimpse of Theo and something unexpected seeded itself at the corner of Gunter's mind, then took root: Gunter loved men.

A book coach by day, Stuart Wakefield writes contemporary romance about men who love men. *thebookcoach.co*

It Takes Two

The skinny girl complains incessantly. The fat girl can't stand it. Finally she gives in and lets the thin girl out.
"Now," the fat girl says. "Let's tango. I've always longed to tango, but it takes two."
The skinny girl hunches her bony shoulders. She doesn't want to tango.

Susi Lovell is a short story writer living in Montreal. *susilovell.com*

Remember?

Babe, can I get something off my chest?
Yes.
Remember that co-worker—the one I always came home talking about? The one for whom basic human decency seemed a tool of Satan?
Yes.
Well, they will NEVER find the body.

Chris Edwards writes stuff and lives in Deep East Texas among the peaceful pines. Facebook *@ChrisEdwardsWriterofStuff*

Summer Passion

Gina fell hard. Like many Summer infatuations, it came on quick and she plunged deep. She gave it body and soul. A desperate, 24/7 obsession.
The crush returned delight and exhilaration.
Then, the painful crash shattered the illusion. Time to move on. Gina gave up her fling with skateboarding.

Bill Diamond writes to try and figure it all out.

A Perfect Life

A barely perceptible expression of fear crosses her face. She's lunching with her best friend. "Meet my colleague, Dr Rashid. You can practice your Arabic." Immediately she asks him to respect her confidentiality. She couldn't tell her friend that, four nights ago, he'd pumped her stomach after she'd tried to kill herself.

Karen Al-Ghabban is a lover of words and languages. Married, two children and a dog.

American Beauty

All summer, Sam listened to the foundry roaring out flames, to the white noise of the chambers churning iron that pulsated like the sun. The sun itself veiled in mystery behind smoke and particulates. A man could gaze directly at her without fear of blindness, and almost forget his breath.

Maryann Lawrence writes poetry, essays and short stories from her home in Southeast Michigan. *MaryannLawrence.net*

Above Your Head, Below The Constellations

Adrian updates the theater marquee. Katie supplies letters. The more controlling he's waxed, the more the allure of his accent has waned. She'd leave him, but, unaccustomed to making her own choices, she's still waiting for a sign. Intruding on her thoughts, Adrian tells her to hand him a zed.

Graham Robert Scott's stories have appeared in *Blink-Ink*, *50-Word Stories*, *The Drabble*, and others. *hemicyon.wordpress.com*

Love

The tree fell, killing his family, who'd enslaved him. He was free to find his real family, whom he aimed to enslave, and keep away from trees. He clear-cut the world in preparation, but never found them. At night, he stares at the moon, dreaming of love and chains.

Allen C. Jones is a California writer and poet living in Norway who doesn't actually believe love is a slavery in certain very special cases. *allencjones.com*

Not Even Tears Will Help

She takes one step. Then two. Three. Four. With each, she expects to rise, lifting, and soaring free. "Take my hands, children," she says, "I will rescue you." She makes a final attempt, but her feet remain stuck in place.
"Why did you believe you could leave me, my dear?"

Cordelia Frances Biddle is the proud recipient of Drexel University's 2021 Adjunct Faculty Award for Teaching Excellence. *cordeliafrancesbiddle.net*

We All Need to Hear That

A part of town not close to me. 24/7. Christmas lights jukebox. Formica tables. Old red plastic upholstery. Ophelia is my waitress. Always. Chesterfields in her apron pocket. She calls me baby. We all need to hear that. "You want eggs with those waffles, baby?"

Christopher Soden likes plump pork chops with cream gravy.

The Athlete

It had never occurred to her before, how athletic she had been. The right prescription administered by the right doctor at the right time seemed to be the right choice. Her cane said otherwise, as the vibrant woman trapped inside her chronically ill body cried out for its former visage.

A.E. Ryan is a writer-publisher at Mount Carmel Publishing and a Silver Winner of the California Film Awards. Twitter *@MountCarmelPub*

Minutes Have Souls

10:15 sits on the photocopy machine and tries to duplicate. The Finance Committee has demanded multiple copies collated with 10:14, 10:13, 10:12—all the minutes since daybreak, nearly three hundred in marching order. The copy machine chugs and groans. There's 10:15 still pressed to the platen glass, pleading for more.

Jackie Craven is the author of the chapbook, *Our Lives Became Unmanageable*, winner of the Omnidawn Fabulist Fiction Award. *jackiecraven.com*

One More Sip

She raised one eyebrow, Spock-like, before removing the mug from my hand.
"That's not decaf," she said.
I winced, shrugged
She let go, creating a splattered stain of coffee and ceramic shards on the driveway.
"Clean it up," she said. "Then get out."
I glanced up and prayed for rain.

Neil Shurley is a member of the American Theatre Critics Association and spends too much time thinking about *Star Trek*. *neilshurley.com*

A Part of Me

"What happened?" I asked as I woke up in the hospital, waiting for an answer but all I got was silence and sad looks. Suddenly, I realized that I felt weak, sore and empty, like I just lost a part of me. "Please, don't tell me I lost another one."

Ezewuzie Nkiruka (PenAlpha) loves writing realistic fictions which does not have a happy ending most times. *asknicki.home.blog*

Terror

Terror grips. I'm high in the air and then plummet face first. A second before crashing to the ground, I'm grabbed and spun once then twice in a high arc. My heart pounds as the car skids to a stop. I get in line to go again.

Christine likes stories that make her pause to appreciate a perfectly worded idea.

A Tale of Two Picnics

The desert, Qatar. I drive to the inland sea with Norwegians, who eat their own food decorously, quietly, in separate family groups. We're home by dark. Next, the Arabs, who pool resources, prepare kebabs and salad together, pitch a tent, light a fire, eat noisily altogether, and leave at dawn.

Karen Al-Ghabban is a lover of words and languages. Married, two children and a dog.

Dinner for Two

Tonight, I made cucumber salad, grilled salmon, and green beans. Too much food for one, so I invited my cute neighbor to share. Wanting to impress, I added slivered almonds to the beans. He didn't notice them until it was too late. Good thing his EpiPen was in his pocket.

Rita Riebel Mitchell writes in NJ and likes to cook for her favorite beta reader who is not allergic to nuts. *RRMitchell.com*

Teeth

I flapped back my cape and met her at the punch bowl. Dry ice melted in a Tupperware bucket. Smoke curled and billowed in the black light. I handed her a cup and she asked, "Don't vampires drink blood?" I removed plastic fangs. We kissed. She bit. Salty. Coppery. Sweet.

Joshua D. Wetjen adores the laughter of his two children and plays jazz guitar and writes short fiction.

The Date

The café he selects is generic and the location irrelevant. You're seated in a narrow passage. Sloping floor tiles grant marginal extra height. When your hot chocolate arrives—in a tall, sort of top-heavy glass—the whipped cream and marshmallows are missing. He and the liquid tilt ominously towards you.

Laura Dobson is currently living in London and is taking the first tentative steps in sharing her work. Twitter @laurarose_13

Law Enforcement

Our neighbor, the cop, has a lawn smooth and uniform as carpet. A lawncare company administers monthly treatments preventing unsightly weeds and unwanted insects, their brochure explains. Our lawn teems with clover, plantain, and dandelions. It's patchy and unpredictable. But at night, it sparkles with fireflies.

Sarah Griffin is a writer living in Central New York, and the managing editor of the occasional online literary publication, *The Elephant. theelephant.press*

Woman in the Hall

There's a woman in the hall who says she can grant us wishes that will give us wealth and power beyond our wildest dreams, and allow us to travel anywhere in this world or beyond, in a matter of seconds, without ever leaving the office. Shall I let her in?

K. T. Maclay is an occasional writer living in the cultural center of Oaxaca de Juarez, Mexico.

Counter Intelligence

The gas station cashier secretly names her memorable customers. Lotto Lady, Rude Dude and You're-Still-Not-21 are regulars. Today, forgetful Hose Guy tells her he drove away while pumping gas. I know, I remember you from last month, she replies. He says, no I did it again. She renames him Call-the-Manager.

Kate Bradley-Ferrall is a writer whose gas station name could be Last Drop Nozzle Shaker. *katebradleyferrall.com*

The Covered Bridge

As the bridge comes into view, my body jolts to a hard stop. It's my first time coming alone—without him. The first time I've felt brave enough to see it again. Or so I thought.
Why did he do it here? Here. This place we came together. Our place.

Melissa Miles is a children's book author, certified educator, registered nurse and board chair of Superhero Success Foundation, Inc. Twitter *@MelissaJMiles*

Mother

She's certain Mother would have found fault. But the garden was perfect. Bordered by yellow iris from the old family home. The fragrant pink roses cascading over an arched trellis. Purple violets now concealing the shallow grave where Mother lay, her cutting words forever silenced by the rich, fertile soil.

Sarah Scott is a chef and writer in the wine country of California. *sarahscottchef.com*

Finding Peace

Sunlight hits a marble column, enhancing blue/gold geometric designs amidst emptiness. Standing, hands cupped, eyes lifted, offering her heart for examination, with perfect grace, her body executes ritual sequences, lips whispering timeless invocations. Cross-legged, drawing her hands quickly over her luminous face, her communion with Allah is complete.

Karen Al-Ghabban is a lover of words and languages. Married, two children and a dog.

Butterfly Powder

"Touching kills butterflies," Momma admonished Leopold, his fingers shimmering with sulfur, his cheeks with accusation. Before the electromagnetic pulse collapsed society, the government vilified the professor who warned against AI control of the grid. Leopold retreated into DNA reanimation. On the first clear day, he started with the butterflies.

Sara Comito is author of the collection *Bury Me in the Sky* (Nixes Mate Books) and a poetry editor for *Bending Genres*. Find her on Twitter *@Comito_writes*

American Dream

Lee was a modern-day American success story. After years of homelessness, he at last had a roof over his head, a warm bed and three square meals a day. He finally had access to medical care, educational classes and job training. At night when he prayed, he thanked God for prison.

Laura Plummer is a writer from Massachusetts whose work has appeared in a number of print and online publications. *lauraplummer.me*

I'm A Little Ghostie

Pam yawned wide. It was late. Time for bed. She switched off the TV and the living room lights. Headed up the stairs. Half way a kid's tune drifted down, followed by a childish giggle. Pam smiled involuntarily and then her brow creased. She doesn't have any children.

Rosie Cullen likes writing all kinds of little stuff but still loves her big novel *The Lucky Country* best.

Terminal

Kirby and his father weren't close. Yet, when Kirby heard his father was terminal, he flew to upstate NY for a last visit. Upon entering the hospital room, Kirby's father raised a jaundiced finger, weakly beckoning his son. Kirby leaned in. His father rasped, "You could've gotten a hair cut."

Geo. Staley lives equidistant from Mt. Hood and the Oregon coast.

Nature is Metal

Hawks take up rotation over the byways, ravishing profligate voles with unyielding voracity. Back-dropped snow-capped mountains complement the crabapple trees fruiting under a clear blue sky. Then someone in the distance yells hello—you friggin' kidding me? Feigning deafness, I shut my eyes, and return to the larger, wilder immensities.

Sal Difalco lives in Toronto, Canada.

Perfect Order

In my next life, I want to live in a cloistered community whose order is devoted to prayer, Gregorian chants, brandy making, hospitality, silence and sock knitting. Once a week we would gossip—but only in writing and only on chalkboards. There would be a strict, convent-wide ban on Chintz.

K. T. Maclay is an occasional writer living in the cultural center of Oaxaca de Juarez, Mexico.

The Nightingale Warning

Anne, motionless beneath her blanket, listened for the telltale chirping of the nightingale floorboards. Her stepfather never fixed the loose planks, as promised. The trilling squeak outside her door was the signal. This night, when he came, Anne would be ready, the hammer gripped tightly in her hand like freedom.

Joseph Austin is a writer and teacher from Forest Hills, New York, where he lives with his husband, Rick, and their dog, Olive.

La Fin

She can't remember disconnecting from the world. The defensive wounds from the theft of her heart and brain have scabbed over. She survives in an empty mind, barely noticing the two daily visitors glancing at their watches as they chat. All three heads nodding in synchrony with her rocking chair.

Diane Minerath lives in Hayden Lake, Idaho and misses her mom.

Excuse Me

I showed the man my photo ID, expecting the usual raised-eyebrow surprise that I was much older than my youthful appearance suggested. But the eyebrows remained level; the face, expressionless. My vain heart sank ... Oh God, I look old ... and wrinkled ... and ugly ... and "Excuse me. Did you say senior discount?"

Jan Bartelli is a former journalist, a more-or-less retired attorney, and a less-is-more writer of creative non-fiction.

Sisters

An innermost voice emerges at long last. "Shine," it says.
Muffled for so long by other voices.
"You take up too much space. You hog too much of the spotlight."
She needed all of the light. My sister. Older than me in age only—
not in the ways that counted.

Melissa Miles is a children's book author, certified educator, registered nurse and board chair of Superhero Success Foundation, Inc. Twitter *@MelissaJMiles*

Time

The door closed and the clamour of other people's troubles faded away. The would-be novelist exhaled the day's distractions. His tiny desk was clear of all but pad and paper. He had exactly ten hours before a warder opened that door again. Ten years times ten hours should be enough.

Avery Mathers writes in the Highlands of Scotland, keeps bees and monitors moths.

Venomenon

Asp Keeper scanned the priority papyrus: "Queen demands asp asap." Ugh. Cecil was on deck. A difficult asp to work with. "Not feeling it, AK," hissed Cecil. "Perhaps," said Asp Keeper, "some curdled rat's milk to ward off the night chill?" Cecil nodded. Asp Keeper smiled. "History shall not forget."

Walt Thomas, author of Smokehouse Stomp, co-hosts the *Charbroiled Chats* podcast.

The Preacher

The preacher slid the flask into a side pocket of his robe, wiped his mouth and stepped into the sanctuary. His shaky faith welcomed the warmth of the spirit spreading through his body and mind. He prayed for the words he needed and counted on the bourbon to deliver them.

Sarah Scott is a chef and writer in the wine country of California. *sarahscottchef.com*

A Breath

Ammonia and bleach equates phosgene, a suffocating chemical gas. Suddenly, I'm gasping, *breathe*! I escape outdoors and slowly collapse. It's peaceful, a pathway of whiteness, friends applaud, cheer and I float toward a refreshing frosty brightness. Wait, these are not my friends. And I hear, "We have a pulse!"

Deb Obermanns is an avid traveler, lover of good books, gelato and lifelong learning. She lives in Germany with her husband and Baci their Affenpinscher.